A SHEPHERD AND HIS FLOCK

A Shepherd and his Flock

Fifty years with Suffolk sheep

KEN RIGGALL

JOHN NICKALLS PUBLICATIONS

Published by John Nickalls Publications,
Oak Farm Bungalow, Suton, Wymondham, Norfolk, NR18 9SH

ISBN 1 904136 27 3 / 978 904136 27 9

PICTURE CREDITS:
Nigel Bloxham p. 56; **G. W. Butcher** pp. 24, 34, 35, 36, 41; **M. Nichols** pp. 33, 38;
Christopher Pipe/Watermark p. 79; **Peter M. Warren** p. 62. Every effort has been
made to trace copyright owners, but the publisher would be glad to hear from
anyone whose photographs may have been used without due recognition so that
acknowledgement may be made in any future edition.

Designed & set in 10½ on 14 pt Palatino Linotype by Watermark, Cromer NR27 9HL

Printed By Barnwell's Print, Aylsham NR11 6ET

Foreword

by Paul Heiney

The life of the traditional working shepherd was always a lonely one, and for that reason it has largely remained a secret. In fact, much about a shepherd's life was a mystery. If it was a choice between flock or family, the true shepherd often gave his sheep the first thought, and if he were to add up the hours spent with them they might far outweigh any human contact he would have. Shepherding was a total way of life, an unfailing commitment. Whatever the season, from the first frosts of autumn, through lambing, to the sticky heat of shearing time, the true shepherd knew his place, and that was with his flock. He knew his sheep as individuals, not in a sentimental way but with a professional detachment which is the mark of a good shepherd. It would be no hardship for him to spend lonely nights in his shepherd's hut, listening for the straining sounds of a difficult lambing, for they were as good as family to him. Modern shepherding is just as skilled, but it is doubtful whether twenty-first-century shepherds would wish to give their entire lives to their flocks. Anway, they don't have to, not with four wheel drives and modern medicines to ease the workload.

This now distant world of traditional shepherding was the one in which Ken Riggall grew up. He was born into a kind of farming that is now almost beyond memory. Then, farms were teeming with a workforce on such a scale that a modern farm manager would faint at the sight of the sheer numbers waiting to be paid at the end of the week. On any decent farm there would be at least a head horseman with several men under him, a stockman or two, several farm workers and, of course, shepherds; each with their particular skills and pride in their work. Ken learnt the hard way how to shepherd sheep, and by writing this memoir he has given us a sharp reminder of how much has been lost in the countryside in the comparatively few years of his lifetime. Ken has seen the horses and horsemen go, the collapse of mixed agriculture as an economically viable way of farming the land, the emergence of corporate rather than individual ways of thinking, leaving the farming landscape almost devoid of human figures.

Despite his struggles, this book remains a celebration of a way of country living that we will never see again. The instinctive powers of the native countryman have been largely lost, and like the bloodlines of the rare breeds of farm animals which have also disappeared it is difficult to see how they can ever be revived. But by setting them out in this book, Ken has made sure that a small piece of rural history has been preserved. And true history it is, because although Ken Riggall's life might not at first appear to be out of the ordinary, the truth is that it is a kind of rural living that will never return. Enjoy this book, and treasure it for the record it provides of a true countryman's life.

Paul Heiney
Suffolk 2006

Dedication

I dedicate this book to my dear wife Patricia, who for the last 50 years and more has been my guiding light, always there when things are not quite going the way you want them to, and putting me back on track. And suddenly I realise that she has had a much rougher passage than me, bringing up four children with very little help from anyone, in living conditions that the young mother of today would not give a second glance to. When I see our children today I feel very proud of the wonderful family I have.

Thank you, Patricia. I could never have achieved my successes without you.

Acknowledgements

Special thanks to Gail Sprake for all the time she has given in helping me with this book. I am sure I would not have attempted it without the help of her and her computer.

Many thanks, too, to the following good people who have been there when a little help was needed: John Taylor; Jim Cresswell; Ian Bradshaw; John Garner.

Contents

The author's grandfather, Charles Riggall

1

Growing up

I was born on 20th October 1922, in a small village in Leicestershire called Scraptoft. I was the third son of my father Charles, who was head gardener at the Manor House in the village. My grandparents were farmers in Lincolnshire, so I guess I must have had working the land in my blood from birth.

By the time I was old enough to run about, I used to go around the farm with the shepherd, Jimmy Jones, in his pony and trap.

My early years were spent in Scraptoft, until my father was offered a better job on the outskirts of Leicester. I was eight years old by then and not looking forward to the move. However, I was quite pleased when we did move, as it was quite near a farm. It was a dairy farm, producing milk and retailing it locally. There were also 1,000 laying hens on the farm. By the time I was 12 years old, I used to go home from school and help to bottle milk, wash the eggs and put the milk through the cooler. I used to get a bottle of milk to take home.

At the weekends I would to go to the farm to collect the eggs, and eventually I was taught how to hand-milk. I got a shilling a day and a pint of milk.

I left school when I was 14 years old, and went to work on the farm full time. I got 17s 6d a week, free milk and half a dozen eggs. My employer at that time was Mr Turner Cooper. He also did mole draining and pit cleaning, so I had to learn how to drive a tractor. His farm manager was Mr Mervyn Philips, and he taught me quite a lot about livestock and general farm work. A year later he moved to a farm on a large estate which was owned by CWS Farms. He asked me to go and work there with him in the next village, a place called Stoughton. The farm was a mixed farm, with cattle, horses and sheep. The sheep became my favourites, though I still had to help with the other livestock. Milking started at 6 o'clock in the morning, and if you were late getting there you had to stop and make your time up before you went home at 5 p.m. By the time I reached the age of 15 I could work with horses, ploughing, harrowing and drilling. I learnt to stack corn and hay and thatch stacks. I could also lay a hedge – this was most important in the Midlands as most farms kept livestock, so the job had to be done properly. I was told that if you couldn't stop a hare going through a hedge then you had not done the job well enough.

By now I had reached the age of 16. As it was a mile or two further to get to work I had to have a bike. My mother bought me a new one, but it was not long before disaster struck. One evening my friend and I cycled to the pictures in Leicester and while we were there some thieving bugger stole my bike, so it was a long walk home, and a long walk to work the next morning. I had to buy an old second-hand bike for £5.

My route to work was through a wood, which saved me about half a mile. Eventually I noticed the large number of rabbits and a few pheasants, and it dawned on me that I could make myself an extra bob or two. I had to get myself some snares, which I knew a bit about as I had watched my older brother setting them. So I started putting down snares on my way home in the evenings, so that hopefully I would have a rabbit or two in the morning. The art of setting snares is to remember how many you had set and exactly where you had set them. The only time we were officially allowed to go rabbiting was on Boxing Day. After a while I got a bit daring and began to set my snares out in the fields, which was much easier. The only problem with this was that if Mr Fox heard a rabbit squealing in a snare, he would be able to find out where it was – then all you would then have left in your snare in the morning would be the rabbit's head! I had to be careful that no one on the farm knew what I was doing, as it would soon have filtered back to higher authorities. So any rabbits I caught had to be gutted and hidden till I went home. I had no trouble selling them

The author (on left, aged 17) with his
younger brother Douglas

down at the Working Men's Club. Before long I was making more money out of selling rabbits than I was getting in my pay packet. One morning I picked up five rabbits and I was quite pleased with myself. I decided to hang them that morning in the pigsty, forgetting that pigs are not fussy about what they eat. When I went to collect them at going home time I found that the bloody pigs had eaten the lot.

Mother, or 'Lil' as my three brothers and I called her, took a very dim view of any misdemeanours. Arriving home late after a good night out was amongst the most serious of crimes. So much so that, after one particularly enjoyable evening, I would have arrived home too late and not sober, so instead I decided to head to the next village and sleep what was left of the night with a friend. It was not easy pedalling the bike in the state I was in, so I abandoned it and collected it the following morning. Being Sunday, I still had to do the morning milking, resplendent in my Sunday suit, before relocating my bicycle and finally heading home. 'Lil' would have no qualms about taking the razor strap to any of us boys if she felt we had justified it.

By this time my brother had joined the Coldstream Guards, and so he passed on to me his ferrets and his double-barrelled 12-bore shotgun. It was a bit different from normal guns: it was called a pinfire, because the cartridges were made with a pin that stuck out at the side at the firing end. The pin protruded through a small hole at the top and when you fired it, a small hammer came down and hit the pin. There was however one little problem – the cartridges were made with black gunpowder. This of course meant that when you fired it there was a huge cloud of smoke, so you had to wait several seconds before you could see whether you had actually hit your target. It was very handy for rook shooting.

Rook shooting was an annual event as you only shot the young rooks as they sat in the treetops. Rook pie is an old country dish, though not to everyone's taste. The best time for shooting young rooks was harvest time. There was no such thing as a combine harvester in those days; the corn was cut with a binder pulled by a pair of horses or, later, a tractor. The procedure was for four men, two with scythes, working in pairs to make a start. The men with the scythes would cut a swathe wide enough for the binder to go round without flattening the corn. Their mates would follow them, bundling the corn that had been cut and tying it up with a band made of corn stalks. They would start at the outside of the crop going round and round the field, and as long as the field was finished by the end of the day you were sure of getting a good lot of rabbits. You needed four guns. As the area of uncut corn got smaller and smaller, the rabbits kept going into the middle of the field. Eventually they had to make a run for it. With a gun on all four sides of the field they had to run pretty quick if they wanted to escape. I remember going home one evening with half a sack full of rabbits and four pheasants on my bike, with my gun tied to the crossbar. When the police stopped me and wanted to know what was in the bag, I told them I had a few rabbits, not mentioning the pheasants. I asked them if they wanted one, as at the time I supplied the Sergeant of Police, who lived opposite me. When I mentioned that they declined my offer and sent me on my way – a good job they didn't want to look in the bag.

The author as an able seaman

2

War service

By now the war clouds were gathering and the young men were being called up. I was told that I would not be called up as working on the farm was a reserved occupation. At first I was quite pleased about this, but as time went by my friends gradually disappeared into the services. By the end of the first year of the war the Land Girls were arriving on the farms so I decided to join up. I went into town and to the recruiting officer. I wanted to join the artillery as I liked the idea of being a gunner. I was told that at the present time they didn't have room for anyone in the artillery, but if I'd like to wait for a few months then they would let me know. So I asked them if I could get into the Navy instead. They seemed quite pleased with that suggestion and I signed up there and then.

I received my call-up papers just after my 18th birthday. I was sent to HMS *Ganges* in Suffolk for six weeks' training, and then on to Chatham, the naval base in Kent. There we had to wait to find out what ship we would be assigned to. Eventually, several of us were told we were going to join HMS *Anson*, a battleship. I was given a short course in gunnery. I found myself in the crew of an anti-aircraft gun situated on the upper deck and we steamed out of Rosyth dockyard, not knowing where we were heading to.

The next day the Captain told us our destination was Iceland. When

HMS Anson

we got there we docked at a naval base just outside Reykjavik. There we were to escort American convoys to Russia. After two spells of six months in the freezing climate where even the seas were freezing over, my shipmate George Judge and myself decided that we had had enough. When a notice came up on the daily bulletin board stating that volunteers were needed for special service we both put our names down. When the ship docked we left it and headed back to Chatham. Upon arrival we were told to check the bulletin board every morning until our names came up with the name of the place to which we would be sent.

Eventually, along with the names of several other ratings, our names appeared, telling us we were going to Quebec for special training. We were very happy about this, but our high spirits didn't last for long once we were put on a train heading to Glasgow. We began to feel a bit doubtful now as Glasgow somehow didn't seem the right direction for Quebec. In fact, it turned out that Quebec was the code name for a naval commando training base at the end of Loch Long – that's how we found out what we had let ourselves in for.

First there was the medical to check how fit we were. Anyone who didn't come up to standard was sent back to Chatham to rejoin a ship. The rest of us were then really put to the sword: route marches with a

On the Russian convoys, 1942

full pack and arms, running up mountains, finishing by jumping off a jetty and swimming back to the shore, still with a full pack. This sort of routine continued for three weeks. By the end of this time you were either fully fit, or bloody useless. After this, the next part of our training was the obstacle course, and if you were still alive and able to run a mile, the next thing we were taught was how to make plastic explosive charges and how to use them.

To our surprise we were then given four days' leave, and told to report back to Inverary Castle on our return. On arriving home I found that Charles, my second older brother, had been called up and had joined the Royal Electrical and Mechanical Engineers. My younger brother Douglas had not had his call-up papers, and he was quite interested in what I had been doing, especially regarding some of the contents of my backpack. He saw that I had some plastic explosive and a detonator, and he wanted to know how it all worked. At that time my father was head gardener for a large hosiery manufacturer in Leicester. His house and gardens were out in the country and covered about 15 acres. We lived in a cottage in the gardens. One of the main features in the centre of the grounds was a large lily pond. The owner and his family were away on holiday at the time, so I told my brother I would show him how the explosives worked. I made the charge up and threw it into the pond. There was a terrific bang. Fish, water, lilies, mud and stones flew everywhere. Needless to say, we beat a hasty retreat. Next morning father came home for his breakfast and told us that the Germans had dropped a bomb in the pond.

After this short break I left for Inverary where our squad joined up with the Canadian 3rd Infantry Division. We were issued with live ammunition to be used in training, so we made good use of this by shooting rabbits. We also made up small explosive charges and threw these into the river; they stunned the fish so we could pick the best ones off the surface of the river. They made a tasty change to the menu of army rations. We also had mutton. The Canadian cooks were pretty good when they found out I worked with livestock. We had to wait for a moonlit night, then I could creep up on a sheep whilst it was sleeping. My helpers would carry it back to the army kitchen; in a matter of minutes it was skinned, dressed and in the copper. All traces of skin and offal were burnt so there were no traces of our night's work to be found.

By this time we began to realise that something big was in the wind, as we were suddenly shipped to the Channel coast. Poole in Dorset was our next base, where we took part in landing exercises on the Isle of Wight. We now knew where we were destined for in the very near future, and my 21st birthday was approaching. On such an occasion your mates all gave you a sip of their rum, this being an old naval tradition. We were not allowed to go out of camp so we had to make our own amusement.

As this was a special party we got slightly tipsy. My mates got together and bet me £5 that I couldn't knock a tin of Spam off the top of the stove at the end of the hut, using my Lewis machine gun from the other end of the hut. By this time I was in the mood for anything, but I had only got to put four bullets in the Spam. I set up the gun and got down on the deck. My mates all stood behind me. Then I took aim and fired. Not only did I hit the tin, but it blew a hole in the end of the hut. I duly collected my £5. Then we had to do a quick repair job on the end of the hut before the Officer of the Watch came round.

At last we were told that we were going to Southampton to get on the landing craft that was to take us to Normandy. The weather was terrible. We got on our boats and set off, only to get half way across the channel and have to turn back as the weather deteriorated. At this time I think most of us were seasick and we could not have cared less where we headed. By the time we got back to Southampton there was no time to get on shore, as we were told that we would be going again before dawn, whatever the weather. The next day was 6th June. And this time there was no turning back. I was as sick as I have ever been, but I soon discovered the quickest cure for seasickness – German bullets as they rattled onto the unloading ramp. At last we were on the shores of Normandy, and as the ramp dropped into the water all hell broke loose, shells and bullets flying everywhere.

We simply ran as fast as we could, hoping there was not a bullet with our name on it. Our friends fell to left and right of us, yet there was nothing we could do for them. Our eyes were fixed on a stone wall about 30 yards up the beach. Our job was to clear the beach of any enemy mines and obstacles, then to put up markers to let the incoming landing craft and infantry know that it was safe to come in. This was not very pleasant, but we had been trained to such a high pitch, we knew it was something that had to be done. It meant losing men, but if we had not done the job it would have meant a lot more men would have died. After we had secured our section of the beach we took a look round to see what was just above the shore line, and to our surprise we found we had landed near a farm. The farmhouse had been knocked about from the naval bombardment, but there was enough of it left for us to be able to make it our headquarters. The only livestock about were cows, but sadly they all lay dead in the fields, except for one which was shut in the barn, along with a turkey and a few chickens. Lucky me, as I was the only one left who knew anything about livestock. All the civilians had been moved further inland. The owner came back after a couple of days and said we could help ourselves to eggs and milk. As I was the only one who could milk a cow and knew anything about hens, I was promoted to temporary farm manager, chief cook and bottle washer, as well as having to do night patrol. This didn't last long as the cow escaped and we never saw any more of her. The hens slowly disappeared. I'll say no more about that, but I had a good idea where they were going.

After a few weeks the Navy had towed a floating dock from England and it was anchored to the beach – it was a brilliant piece of seamanship. Everything could be loaded onto lorries and driven straight to the front line. After a few weeks, supply lines had been established and there was no longer any fear of a counter-attack from the Germans. We were told we were to be shipped back to England as we were needed in another part of the world, but we had to have replacements and be re-kitted for jungle training. We were not very happy about this. We had to go under canvas, camping on the marshes at Kessingland in Suffolk. We were not told where we were heading, but we had a pretty good idea. As things were going well in Europe the only place we could be sent was the Far East. After a short spell of leave and more training, we were told officially that we would be going out to the East. Fortunately for us time dragged by and VE Day was declared. Not long after that the Yanks dropped the atom bombs on Japan and we finished up working on a farm just outside Lowestoft in Suffolk, harvesting sugar beet and mangolds. It wasn't so long afterwards that that we were sent up north to an army camp to wait our turn to be demobbed.

Before I close this chapter of my life I'd just like to tell you one more amusing thing. I had heard that all the officers were to attend a meeting in Lowestoft so we decided we would do a bit of fishing. A stream ran through the marshes where we were camped and the marshman had a boat tied up close by. I made up half a dozen small charges; then I realised I hadn't got any detonators, but I knew where they were in the officers' quarters. I nipped in through the window, grabbed half a dozen and away we went. After we had dropped a couple of charges in, we had got a couple of buckets of carp and decided that that was enough. We tied the boat up and returned to camp. Then trouble met us face to face: one of the officers had returned and wanted to know where we had been and where we got the explosives from. Well, the long and the short of it was that I was called before the CO the next morning to explain my actions. I thought I might as well tell him the truth rather than spin him a yarn. His reply was did I want to take my punishment from him or go before the captain. I had no hesitation in answering that one. I was confined to camp for seven days and lost two days' pay. It could have been a lot worse.

Two weeks later we were transferred up to Catterick and demobbed the following week.

A traditional Suffolk ram of the 1950s.
Note the smaller head, a similar size to the ewe's head of today, without the
massive bone of today's Suffolk. This lamb was Champion Single Ram Lamb at
the Ipswich Show and Sale, sold for 400 guineas and exported to Canada.

3

Becoming a shepherd

On arriving home I found that my father's employer had sold his house and gardens and bought a smaller place, so we had to move. From living out in the country we had to move into a street of terraced houses in the village of Oadby, about three miles outside Leicester. I was still able to go back to my work on the farm, but on my return to work I couldn't see that much had changed, except that the milking was now done by machine. I was not sorry about that.

I put up with my old job for about a year. Then I went to see the Estate Manager to ask whether there was any chance of promotion. He replied that there was little chance of that and asked me what I wanted to do. I told him that I wanted to specialise in pedigree sheep breeding. He said that there were no pedigree flocks in the area but if I was prepared to move to East Anglia then there were plenty of Suffolk sheep flocks down there. His advice was to carry on with my present job and in the meantime look out for a vacancy, which he would then try and find out about. I agreed to this.

It was during this spell of waiting for something to turn up that something very special occurred. Every morning after milking I had to take the milk up to Home Farm where the lorry picked it up to take it into Leicester. My transport was a pony and float. On this particular morning I was going up to the collecting point when I saw a young lady ahead of me. As I trotted by I thought I recognised her, so I turned round to take another look, and fell out of the float. That was the start of my courting days. I really did fall for her – out the back of the milk float! Patricia was her name and I hadn't seen her since I joined the navy in 1941.

About six months later I received a letter inviting me to go for an interview for a job in Essex as assistant shepherd with the pedigree Suffolk flock owned by Mr Stanley Webb, who farmed at Abbots Hall, Horsley Cross, near Manningtree in Essex. I was asked a lot of questions about what I knew of sheep and whether I could shear. When I said I could, Mr Webb leaned back in his chair and asked me when I could start. I couldn't believe what I was hearing. We went out to the sheep where I was introduced to the head shepherd, Dick Smith. We seemed to hit it off straightaway. At last, I thought, I have my foot on the first rung of the ladder. I asked Mr Webb about living quarters and he told me he had some lodgings in the next village. We then returned to his house for a meal and I was told to go home and sleep on what we had discussed and then phone him back the next day. He told me the job was mine, but I had to let him know within 24 hours as there were at least 20 more young men who had applied for the post. Well, I phoned him the very next morning and told him I could start the next week. That was how I became a shepherd.

The only thing I didn't think much of was my lodgings. I went to live with a couple, and I can safely say that it was not like home. To say the food was uninteresting would be kind to them, since the staple diet appeared to consist solely of rabbit. Rabbit for lunch and rabbit for supper, day in and day out. It was so bad that I told Mr Webb I would rather live in a tent. The only good thing about it was that it was next to a pub, suitably named the Live and Let Live. Then I had a brainwave. On the farm there was a shepherd's hut, complete with bunk bed and a coal fired stove near the door. Under the bed was a space which was used for any sickly or cold lambs in need of extra warmth for a short while. (After I was married any weak lambs went in to the kitchen and were kept warm by the stove in the house.) At one time it used to be towed behind a steam engine when travelling round from farm to farm threshing corn; the driver of the steam engine used to live in it. Now it was only used at lambing time, as I was to find out. Lambing started on 1st January, so the shepherd spent 24 hours a day in a yard made of straw, sleeping in the hut. I asked Mr Webb if I could make use of the hut and he agreed, as he did not want me to leave. I had an arrangement with the wife of the farm foreman, Mrs Fairhead. She would cook me one hot meal a day and do a bit of washing for me.

Sadly this arrangement did not last for long. Poor old Dick the head shepherd was taken ill with cancer and died soon after. I was shocked at this. Having only been with this wonderful flock for such a short time, what was I to do? Mr Webb solved the problem. He asked me if I felt capable of taking charge of the flock. I replied that I could manage the running of the flock, but that I had not done any trimming or showing. That wouldn't be a problem, he said, since he knew a top shepherd who had recently retired and he could get him to come to me one day a week to show me the art of preparing sheep for shows. His name was Charlie Lampard; he was one of the top showmen in the country and he lived in Ipswich. A taxi used to collect him each week and take him home again after his day with me. He was a very clever man, and I knew as soon as he set to work that if I couldn't learn from what he showed me, then I couldn't learn from anybody. You learn more by watching and then having a go yourself than just by asking questions, so after Charlie had gone home I used to go and get a lamb out that was going to the butcher and practise on that. I was quite surprised how much time you had to spend on one sheep. As with most things in life, practice makes perfect. I got the hang of trimming quite quickly but I would certainly not say I was an expert straightaway. I am a great believer in the old saying that you are never done learning.

In the meantime Dick Smith's widow and daughter decided to move away, so the cottage became vacant. As it was a tied cottage I was given the opportunity to move in, so Patricia and I decided that the best thing for us to do was to get married and set up home. We had not been able to see much of each other over the past 12 months – it was rather a long way to go courting from Manningtree to Leicester. We fixed the wedding date for 14th October 1949.

Ken and Patricia on their wedding day

After a short honeymoon in Lowestoft we moved into our new home. There was no bathroom – we had to have the tin bath in front of the fire and heat the water in a copper out in the shed. The toilet was outside; it was the bucket type which I had to empty myself after digging a hole in the garden. There was a small sink in the kitchen, with a bucket underneath to catch the water. And there were no drains. Not much to bring a new bride home to, especially as she had come from a modern home, but that's what you call true love. We did have one piece of good luck: one of the men who worked on the farm was leaving and he asked me if I would like to buy his furniture. In those days you could only purchase furniture on tokens, so I bought the whole lot for £100.

A lot of people still think that all shepherds are the same as far as the job of shepherding is concerned. This is far from the truth. There is the commercial shepherd who spends his day with large flocks of crossbred sheep on the moors and mountains of the North of England, Wales and Scotland. These shepherds produce fat lambs and breed crossbred ewes.

Then there is the shepherd who spends his time breeding pedigree ewes to produce rams and show sheep. In the 1940s and 1950s most of these flocks were in East Anglia, and kept on arable farms. The Suffolk sheep was the prominent breed. They were known as the sheep with the golden hooves, because they were folded on the light lands and enriched the soil with what they left behind them. The head shepherd had a page whose job it was to set a fresh fold every day on whatever food was available. Setting the fold meant setting up wooden hurdles and three-foot-high sheep netting. The netting came in rolls of 50 yards. The wire was used for the sides of the fold; each roll required 15 wooden stakes. Twenty-five wooden hurdles were then set across between the two nets to complete the square. Using three rows of hurdles you could move the back row up after the sheep had cleaned up the food in the first fold. A good shepherd needed to have a good pair of shoulders, as he was expected to carry a 50 yard roll of net on his back supported by two stakes, one on each shoulder, and a dozen stakes on his chest. This was one of my many tasks when I started to learn about what is known as arable shepherding. Most of the flocks of Suffolk ewes were in the range of 200 animals, so you can see there was always plenty of work to be done.

Ninety per cent of the food was grown fresh each year. The yearly programme of crops for the sheep was planned a year ahead and you never went on the same piece of land again until there had been three arable crops on it. Good farming in those days had to be done on a four-crop rotation: wheat, barley, sugar beet and cabbage. The cabbages were an early variety called January King and they served a double purpose. A local market gardener came and took half of them and they were sent to London, leaving the rest for the sheep. It worked out quite well, and following that there were three or four acres of kale. This took us into April, by which time a maiden layer of grass was nearly ready. The grass had been undersown in last year's barley.

Following this, in July came winter tares. Spring tares took us into August, by which time the ewes had been weaned and were being flushed on permanent grass meadows ready for tupping. As soon as the lambs

Lambs folded on cabbages, late January

were old enough to eat solid food, a creep hurdle was placed in the fold so that the young lambs could go forward and eat the best of the green feed. The lambs also had a corn trough in their creep area. The creep hurdle and the troughs were moved forward every day and the ewes came up behind to clean up what the lambs had left.

Whilst this gives an idea of the daily routine, there were many other jobs to be done. Lambs had to be vaccinated against pulpy kidney. Tails had to come off. This is a procedure which if it were carried out today you would most certainly have the RSPCA after you. Nowadays it's all done with rubber rings. In my younger days it was a different kettle of fish altogether. First, you had to build a good fire, mostly of broken hurdles which were kept over the year just for that purpose. We had a set of three or four tailing irons. These were about 18 inches long, with a wooden handle at one end and a two-inch blade at the other which tapered off to form a sharp blade. These were stuck into the fire to warm them up (well, a bit hotter than warm, let's just say rather hot). The next item was a tailing stool about four feet long with two good sturdy legs at each end. The final piece of equipment was an oil can containing the shepherd's special concoction of healing oils and iodine. It was a four-man job as the lambs were about ten weeks old and the tails were fairly big. People might ask why we didn't do them sooner. Well, the reason for that was that there were no such things as rubber rings in those days and you could not use a knife as there were tetanus germs in the soil. As soon as the shepherd considered that the tailing irons were hot enough, the shepherd's assistant sat on the end of the stool holding the lamb between his knees. The lamb had to be sitting up facing the shepherd, who then took the hot iron from the fire. Gripping the end of the lamb's tail, the shepherd would stick the hot blade in the appropriate position. The tail was off before the lamb knew what was happening; a squirt of oil and off they went. Not many people today would believe you if you told them that quite a few of the old-time shepherds and their families always took some of the bigger tails home. I never did really find out what they did with them; the only thing I could guess was that they made a stew or soup with them.

It was now 1950. Shearing and dipping were taking place and the show season was approaching. There were no permanent showgrounds in those days. My first show of the year was the Essex County Show at Saffron Waldron. I surprised everyone, including myself, when I won the class for a pen of ewe lambs. My lambs beat the ewe lambs which had won the championship at the Suffolk Show in Ipswich the previous week. They belonged to Sir Robert Gooch of Benacre Hall in Suffolk.

The next show was the Tendring Hundred Show in Essex, where we won three classes: ram lambs, ewe lambs and shearling ewes.

Then came the Suffolk Sheep Sale at Ipswich in July. At that time this was the most important sale of Suffolk Sheep in the whole country, where all the top breeders bought their rams for breeding. Mr Webb entered ten rams. In the show prior to the sale I was amazed to win first prize and champion for a single ram lamb. This ram lamb later sold for 400 guineas, to a breeder from Canada. I also won second prize for a pen of three ram lambs. Mr Webb's consignment averaged £110 for the ten sheep entered, which was a lot of money in those days.

The next major operation was getting all the rams ready to travel round the sheep sales. This entailed trimming day after day, and hopefully coming home with an empty lorry after each sale. In between sales the ewes were split up into four groups, and a ram was put into each group according to the pedigrees. The rams were officially put in on 7th August each year, so if all went well you would start lambing on 1st January. A lot of lambs were born before that date. There was an old saying amongst the shepherds at the shows: 'I bet that lamb saw the Christmas dinner.'

It was during the time I spent preparing the rams for sale that I met my first celebrity. If it was fine weather I did all the trimming outside, as the wool was much better to work on when the sun shone. One morning a gentleman came riding by on his horse. He passed the time of day with me and said he hoped his horse didn't frighten the sheep. He introduced himself as Mr Alfred Munnings; he later became Sir Alfred Munnings. Like my employer, he was a keen hunting man. What a pity I didn't get him to paint me at work – I might have been worth a bob or two now!

In October the National Suffolk Flock Competition took place.

Shepherds at the Tendring Hundred Show, 1950
shearling ewe class
(the author, seen far right, won 1st and 2nd prizes)

Prominent members of the society were the judges, Mr Bocock, Mr Rush and Mr Giles. The results would not be announced for some time as they had to travel all round the country to judge all the other flocks. It was usually not until mid-October that the results were published. My birthday falls on 24th October, and whether it was just coincidence I shall never know, but that particular day Mr Webb came round on his morning gallop with a smile on his face. He told me that we had won the double: the national championship and Gold Cup for the best flock of ewes, and the Frank Sainsbury Cup for the best ewe lambs. I could not have wished for a better birthday present. This meant an open day on the farm for flock owners and shepherds to come and have a look at our flock, attend the presentation and have a drink. What a start to my new life. I was a very happy young man. And to top it all my very special wife presented me with our first baby. We named him Charles Harold after his grandfather.

It was now coming up to 1951. It was time to prepare for lambing and build the lamb yard. This was sited on a different field each year. The first stage of this operation commenced during harvest. In those days there were no combines; the corn was tied up in sheaves, then stood up in stooks for a period of time known as 'three church bells', meaning three Sundays. It was then stacked at the farm in what was called the stack yard, an area kept especially for that purpose. The stacks were built in pairs leaving just enough room for the threshing drum to get between them. Then the stacks were thatched to keep out the rain. Two stacks were built where the lambing yard was to be situated, one facing north and the other facing east. They were then threshed and the straw tied into bundles and stacked to form two sides of the lamb yard. Wooden sheep hurdles were then placed round the inside to form pens for each of the ewes as they lambed. Hurdles were laid across the top of the pens and bundles of straw placed on top to give protection from the weather.

Shepherds 1951. Lleft to right: George Bailey (shepherd for Mitchell Bros), Albert Hunt and assistant (for John Long), ?, ?, Bert Eyeson (for Pauls at Kirton Lodge), Harald Rush (for Sir Robert Gooch), Charlie Peck (for John Jiggens), ?, Ted Erith (assistant shepherd for Sir Robert Gooch), Charlie Lampard (retired), ? (shepherd for the Yeldham flock), the author and his dog Flash, Bill Clarke

I always looked forward to lambing time. It was the start of a new year and new life. It always gave me a good feeling, seeing the new lambs arriving. It also meant you were at work 24 hours a day for a few weeks. I used to snatch an hour's sleep in the shepherd's hut which stood at the lamb yard gate, dashing home for a wash and a quick meal when things in the yard were quiet. Most shepherds who have spent their lives with their sheep will tell you, and I have found it to be true, that if you walk

National Champion ewe lambs 1951. All were destroyed later that year because of foot and mouth disease

amongst the ewes once they have come into the yard for the night, you can tell which ones will lamb before morning. The older ewes especially would hang on to their lambs until they got onto the straw where it was a bit warmer. The maiden ewes lambing for the first time would drop their lambs anywhere they could. If they were going to have twins they would drop the first lamb and then wander off and give birth to the other one some distance away, so you had to be there to take the first lamb to her. Each sheep had a pen to herself once she had lambed, and she would spend three or four days there, depending upon whether she had one or two lambs. It gave you a chance to check that she had milk and make sure the lambs were sucking. Eventually they would all go out during the day and be shut back in the yard at night. This system continued until the end of March, after which time the yard would be dismantled and the sheep would go on to their usual folding routine.

The Abbots Hall flock, Gold Medal winners

1951

Owners, judges & shepherds. Left to right: Bob Giles (judge), ?, Arthur Webb, the author, Stanley Webb, Mr Rush (the judge, standing behind), ?, Bob Tyte

1950 had been a most successful year and I was feeling very pleased with myself. They say all good things come to an end. By the end of March the sheep had been lying out at night for about a week. I went to feed them. It is a date I shall never forget, 2nd April 1951. I went into the field where the ewe hoggets were (hogget is a term used to describe ewe lambs that are kept from last year as replacement females for old ewes that would be culled later in the year). Several of these ewe hoggets failed to get up and come to the trough. I went to see what was wrong with them, but there was no outward sign of anything the matter with them so I left them alone. I came back later and all the sheep were lying together so I assumed things were all right. The next morning I noticed that several more of the hoggets did not come and feed. By now I was really worried and when Mr Webb came round on his morning ride I told him I would like the vet to come and have a look at them. The vet arrived in due course, looked at the sheep and his verdict was that they had foot-rot, so we had to put them through the foot bath. I was not particularly happy with this diagnosis but had to take the vet's word for it.

Things got worse. As there had been an outbreak of foot and mouth disease 17 miles away I told Mr Webb that we should have a second opinion. He called the Ministry vets to come and take a look. On their arrival it didn't take many minutes for them to confirm my own opinion, that our sheep had foot and mouth. I was devastated. They ordered a gang of butchers to slaughter them as soon as possible. A large hole was dug in the field and they were all buried that same day. The pit was filled with quicklime and covered over immediately; there was no burning of carcases in those days. The farm was closed off for three weeks. All remaining stock on the farm that showed no sign of disease were sent off to slaughter straightaway, for human consumption. I went to bed that night and could not sleep; I just thought it was a bad dream, until I looked out of the window and could not see a live animal anywhere out in the fields.

So ended my first venture into pedigree sheep breeding. Mr Webb was shattered; he said he could never build up another flock like the one we had just lost; in fact, he never did re-stock the farm, but kept only his horses after that. The life went out of the farm, but he told me I could stay on the farm and work until another job came along.

News of the disaster spread quickly, as did the fact that Mr Webb would not be starting another flock and I would therefore be looking for another job. In the meantime foot and mouth disease spread too, to another pedigree flock in the next village belonging to Mr Hayward. His shepherd, Sam Hurst, was a friend of mine and we used to go out to shows and sheep sales together. Sam was a bit of a worrier at the best of times and I know he took the loss of the flock very badly.

1st prize single ram lamb (trimmed), Tendring Hundred Show

4

Kirton and Sutton Hoo

By this time I had been approached by the Estate Manager from Mr Stuart Paul's estate in the village of Kirton in Suffolk. He asked me if I would be interested in taking charge of the Kirton flock as his current shepherd was retiring. I agreed but said I would like to have a look at the place before giving my final answer. He arranged to pick me and my wife up the following week. On arriving at Kirton we discovered it was quite near the seaside at Felixstowe. I didn't know at that time that Charlie Lampard who had taught me to trim was shepherd to this flock before he retired, but that the flock had gone downhill since he had left. I asked where we would be living and was shown the semi-detached cottage. The old shepherd was still living there at the time and I asked him if he would mind if we had a look round. He invited us in.

Well, it wasn't much better than the cottage we were living in at the time – the only water supply was a well outside the back door, the toilet was outside and you still had to wash in a tin bath in the kitchen. I think the only thing that persuaded us to accept the job was the fact that it was near the sea and within ten minutes' walk of the river Deben. It also gave me the chance to improve my experience in my work. It was not until we moved in to the cottage that we discovered what the inside was really like. It was infested with mice and I wouldn't like to guess when it had last had a good clean. I had never seen so many rats out in the garden.

I had a word with the gamekeeper and we worked out a deal: if he could get rid of the rats I'd deal with the mice. It took me a fortnight to make the place habitable. I never saw Mr Paul to be able to complain about the state of the house and I knew it wasn't much good saying anything to the farm manager. It hadn't taken me long to weigh him up: he was more concerned with lining his own pocket than spending anything on other people. Patricia and I decided we would not give in, so we dug our toes in and did the best we could. However, I couldn't see the situation lasting very long unless the people at the top were prepared to give a hand.

The flock of Suffolks, 200 head, needed a lot of money spent on rams and it would take some considerable time to get the flock looking like it used to. My first show with this flock was at the Suffolk County Show at Benacre Hall in 1953. I managed to get among the prizes but there were no red cards.

My next show was the Royal Show, held that year in Blackpool. The Benacre flock was winning everything that year. Harald Rush was the top shepherd amongst the Suffolk flocks, so I was quite pleased to come away with three second prizes. I spent a further three years at Kirton and I never really enjoyed my time there. If you are not happy in your work you cannot give of your best.

The only bright light during that time was when Patricia told me she was expecting, and produced a daughter, Wendy, born on 16th December 1954.

One other event worth mentioning during my time at Kirton was the East Coast floods. I woke up one morning to see 500 acres of marshes under water. Fortunately the ewe flock was on high ground. If it had happened a week earlier they would all have been drowned. Shortly after that, myxomatosis appeared in the wild rabbit population. That didn't trouble me too much because I kept tame rabbits which I bred for the local market. I never expected them to take any harm – but I was wrong. One morning Pat came up to my sheep shed and told me there was something wrong with the rabbits. I went to have a look and to my dismay they all had the disease. I was told later that flies from the wild rabbits had spread it.

It was coming up to Christmas and it would soon be lambing time again. I had one more sideline to see to before lambing got started. I kept a

With Don Garwood at Ipswich Ram Sale 1950;
the author won 2nd prize

few cockerels and fattened them for Christmas. I had learnt to pluck and dress poultry as a boy, and wherever I moved to someone always seemed to find out about this skill and so I always got asked if I would do their birds for their Christmas dinners. I seemed to get quite a variety of birds as well as cockerels – pheasants, geese and turkeys. I didn't mind this job as it gave me an extra bit of pocket money which was always useful at this time of the year. It was round about this time that our daughter Wendy was born, so I decided to go to the pub to wet the baby's head. I must have had one or two, too much anyway, and feeling good, I walked home. I went into my shed to finish the plucking, but I can't remember how long I was in there as I must have dozed off and fell off my plucking stool into the pile of feathers. According to my mother-in-law I looked a pretty sight as I walked down the garden towards the house covered in white feathers from head to toe.

I made up my mind that the coming year, 1955, would be my final year in this situation as my employer had decided he would not be prepared to spend any money on the house. I didn't think the place was fit for Patricia and two young children, so as I went out on the usual round of shows and sales, I let people know that I was looking for a new job.

It wasn't long before I had several offers; the one that interested me most was from Mrs Barton, who was just setting up a flock at Sutton Hoo. Her farm was just the other side of the river Deben, near Woodbridge. I went to see her for an interview. She had a second farm at Ufford, also near Woodbridge. Her flock consisted of 50 Suffolk ewes which she had purchased from Lord Ellesmere, who farmed an estate at Stetchworth, near Newmarket, and who had decided to sell his flock. I knew the shepherd who worked with the flock at the time – his name was Fred Samms – and he had been with the Stetchworth flock for a long time. The reason Mrs Barton was looking for a younger man was because she understood that Fred was not a well man and she needed someone with experience to take over when Fred packed up, which she didn't think would be very long. We agreed on the money and what I was to do, as long as it did not upset Fred. Then the only thing left to do was to look at the state of the house that came with the job, and where it was. We got into the car and she drove me down to the other farm she owned at Ufford. The house was opposite the Crown pub, and had once been the farmhouse for the other farm. Patricia could not get inside quickly enough; surely it must be better than the last two we had lived in. We opened the door and then we just stood and stared – it was a real modern house.

'Look! A real toilet, a bath and water out of a tap!' Pat exclaimed. The house alone was enough to convince me. Pat would have liked to have moved in the very next day, but I had to give notice that I was leaving Kirton, so she would have to wait a little longer. A shepherd's year unofficially ends when he has sold the last of his rams, which can be the end of September and the middle of October. By then the breeding sales have come to an end as far as the pedigree flocks are concerned. That is the time when you see shepherds looking for fresh jobs.

The only reason we were sorry to be leaving Kirton, despite the primitive living conditions, was that the area surrounding the house was beautiful, if a little bit isolated. We would miss our walks by the river and the woodland; it was very quiet and peaceful and you never had to worry about the children.

We made our move in October, and once we had got into the house at Ufford, it all seemed worthwhile. We had very good neighbours, John and Margaret White. John worked on the farm with the cattle and we got on quite well. With the pub across the road things began to look better every day. Fred and I got along very well together; I suppose the reason for that was that I was doing all the heavy work. But one day I really did upset him. He was a man who was very keen on showing, and so was I. His favourite show was the Smithfield Show, in Earl's Court, London. For this show Fred had persuaded Mrs Barton to buy some Southdown sheep, and he asked me to shear them for him. However, it was very different from shearing Suffolks. They had wool everywhere and you had a job to see their eyes and ears. Unfortunately, I took my mind off the job I was doing and when I got to the sheep's head I clipped an ear clean off. Fred was livid. I wouldn't like to put into print what was said, but the air was blue for a few minutes as this was a ewe he intended to show next year. To add to the extra strong language, blood shot everywhere. Still, after Fred had had two or three cigarettes he settled down. I told him that if he wasn't careful he would have a heart attack.

The New Year was just around the corner and lambing time was upon us again. Of course, I was detailed for that job as according to Mrs Barton it would not be safe for Fred to be left on his own all night. I was advised to lock the hut up when I was in the sheep yard, and lock my bike up too, as we were not too far away from Hollesley Bay Prison. If any of the boys escaped, which they did very frequently, they had to pass close to where we were and apparently they would pinch anything they could lay their hands on.

Work for me was going well; in fact, it was a case of finding something to keep me occupied at times as by now we had another 'recruit', a young local man set on as tractor driver and general help. So Fred had even less to do. I could see that he was looking much better, and so he should, with three of us looking after 60 sheep.

The Suffolk and the Essex Shows passed off with satisfactory results; then came the Royal Show, which this year was held at Swindon. I had to go ahead with the sheep, and Fred followed on with Mrs Barton. We had quite a good show: two firsts, three seconds and the reserve Champion. The next day I was left at the show on my own to feed and look after the sheep, and a lorry would come and pick me up with the sheep at the end of the show.

A week or so afterwards, I started to have what I would call blackouts. I would go to bed feeling fine but during the night I was doing a bit of sleepwalking. I would wake up in the bathroom, or in other parts of the house, and I was not able to remember even getting out of bed. Well, to cut a long story short, I went to see the doctor. He couldn't find anything wrong with me so I was sent up to Ipswich Hospital to see a specialist who examined me from head to toe, and he couldn't find anything wrong with me either. He then told me to open my mouth and he asked me what I did for a living. I told him I was a shepherd, and he immediately asked me if I used any chemicals. I told him that the only thing we used was what we put in the foot bath, which contained arsenic.

'Well, unless you want to go to an early grave, you had better stop using it sooner rather than later,' I was sharply told. 'You have been inhaling poisonous fumes.'

The consultant gave me a mirror and pointed out the blue line around my gums. He gave me some antibiotics and said he would write to the manufacturer and tell them to take the chemical off the market before someone was poisoned. This was 1956.

With Fred's health improving, I could not see much future as things stood, though I never said anything about it to anyone at that time. But I was thinking of my future nevertheless.

5

Lackford

I was out at a show the following year when I was approached by Mr D. W. P. Gough, who lived at Lackford Manor and farmed a large estate in the village. He had a large flock of Cluns as well as a flock of Suffolks which he had not had for very long. He used to have a flock of Southdowns too. His shepherd was Philip Wadman, a very good shepherd and a nicer man you could not wish to meet.

The story goes that Philip was a Southdown man born and bred, and came from Devizes in Wiltshire. I do not think he was very fond of Suffolk Sheep. Most shepherds once they start their career with a certain breed of sheep don't like change. Sometimes it works, but different breeds have different feeding habits and different wool; no two breeds are alike. Mr Gough said that he had heard that I was not settled with what I was doing at the time, playing second fiddle to Fred, and he asked me whether I would be interested in taking on his flock. I said I dared say I could be persuaded, and was told that if I was interested I was to let him know within 24 hours. I gave him a ring the following day and said that my wife and I would like to come and have a look around. He told me to take a taxi; he would pay the fare and a day's wages. That couldn't be bad for a start, I thought.

The first thing we saw on our arrival at Lackford was a new house he

The author with lambs and ewe, about 1957

had built for his shepherd. He took me to look at the sheep. It was then I discovered that he had bought the entire flock from Mr Goodchild of Yeldom, Essex. The flock had been founded in 1906 by his father and had been in the family ever since, making it one of the oldest Suffolk flocks in the breed. We had a look around the farm and I was very impressed with what I saw. He told me not to tell him there and then whether I would take the job, but to go home and sleep on it. I didn't think there was any need for that, the only thing that worried me was what Mrs Barton was going to say. I rang her that night and told her of my decision. She was quite upset and came down to me the next morning to try and persuade me to change my mind and stay. However, I told her it was too good an opportunity to miss and that it would be great to be in charge of a flock once again.

I telephoned Mr Gough to tell him I would take the job at the end of September. He was extremely pleased about this and said that I was to let him know when I was ready to move and he would arrange for a removal firm to come and bring our furniture over to Lackford. This was to be move number three. There's an old saying about a rolling stone gathering no moss, but I was sure in my own mind that this was not going to be the case with me. Hopefully I was going to work for a gentleman who knew all about farming and sheep. It makes a lot of difference to a shepherd if his employer knows a fair bit about the job and yet is still prepared to listen to you and agree with your decisions.

But don't forget that you have to show good results if you want to be successful. I made a good start by coming second in the 1959 Farmer and Stockbreeder National Lambing Competition. The Suffolk flock of 160 ewes reared 254 lambs, which included 19 sets of triplets. I learnt a lot from that experience. You don't need all those triplets if you are showing and selling rams. A good single would be a lot better, but you cannot be sure of that; if you lose a single then you have a ewe with nothing to do for the next 12 months. The only way out of that is to skin the dead single lamb and put the skin on an orphan lamb, or on one of those triplets that you didn't want in the first place. Then introduce the 'new' lamb to the mother who has just lost her single lamb.

1960 was around the corner and lambing time was upon us again. We had a good fall of lambs, but not so many this year; thank the Lord for that. It makes the job so much easier if you can walk round and see all your lambs lying in the pens with their mothers, with a belly full of milk.

This year the shows started in May, with the Hertfordshire and Cambridgeshire shows. Little did I know what was to be the outcome. I won all four classes at the Hertfordshire Show and a week later we toddled off to the Cambridge and Isle of Ely Show. If my memory serves me right this was held at Histon. I had just won the first three classes when I was told that Mr Gough had been taken ill and had had to go home. When I got home that night I learnt that he had had a heart attack and was in hospital in Bury St Edmunds. He remained in hospital for some time, missing both the Suffolk Show and the main Suffolk Sheep Sale in Ipswich. I missed his presence, as we had a very good understanding of what was right and what was wrong. I was taken to see him and had to report on how things were going with the sheep. I was pleased to be able to report that everything was going according to plan.

The next event was the second Suffolk Sheep Sale, held at Bury St Edmunds cattle market. For some reason this sale was known as the Horringer Fair, but I never did find out why it got that name. It always took place around the end of August. We entered 12 ram lambs. These rams were mostly destined for the commercial market. I had another very successful day in the showing classes. I won the Ellesmere Cup for the best single lamb, which then sold for 175 guineas. And just to make it an even better day I then won the Paul Cup for the best pen of three ram lambs, which sold individually for 100 guineas, 115 guineas and 135 guineas. The average price paid for the 12 rams I brought to the show was 74 guineas, so as this was 1960 it wasn't a bad day's work. Mr Gough's son Dick was now the man I had to answer to as his father was still ill and back in hospital again. Dick told me to get the smell of sheep off me as I had to go and see his father and tell him the good news about the sheep as he needed cheering up a bit.

Sadly, Mr Gough died later that year, and he was greatly missed by everyone in the farming community. I knew life would not be the same at Lackford without him, and I missed him very much. I also knew that whoever I knew and worked for in the future, he or she would have to be something special.

Life continued. Another new year and the show season continued its usual pattern. This year an extra show was added to our list, the Lincolnshire Show. I hoped that I would still continue to make a name for myself as a showman and would be able to produce something to please the judge's eye. Going up to Lincolnshire gave me an extra incentive, as at that time it was the only county in which the name Riggall was to be found. From information I have gathered over the years my ancestors were exiled from Normandy in the 1560s. They landed in this country and commenced farming here, though I don't think you will find the name anywhere else even to this day. I did quite well at the Lincolnshire

Show – not only was I among the winners, but I met some relatives I didn't know existed.

Back to work with the sales around the corner. With a good show season behind you it gives you extra confidence. It's like a shop window: if you have a good display you can attract the buyers and that is half the battle. We made a good start with a consignment of males and females going over to France. The Suffolks seemed to be catching on over there. I was told that sheep heading over to France had to be vaccinated and blood tested. I told M Columbet of the Fédération Nationale Ovine in Paris that at that time they had every disease under the sun over in France, so there wasn't much chance of sheep from England taking anything else over there.

The final count-up of major prizes for the year was 16 first prizes and three championships, and to top this we won the national flock competition. My only regret was that Mr Gough was not alive to see it. Following this success came an order from South Africa for ten ewes and one ram. Sales like this were much better than hawking the sheep round the country and getting what you could for them.

In the meantime, Mr Dick, as we used to call him, had decided to sell the commercial flock. This was fine by me as the chap who used to help with the Cluns then moved over to become my assistant. Billy Plant was a good worker who, like me, liked a pint, especially if it was free. This brings me to a rather amusing story: we were folding the ewes on a field of white clover in a quiet corner of the farm hidden from the road by trees. We noticed an old cottage and decided to take a closer look. We discovered that an oldish man of rather rough looking appearance resided there on his own; we got chatting to him and learnt that he kept bees, which he used to cart around the countryside from clover fields to orchards. During the course of our conversation he asked whether we would like a glass of mead. We naturally replied in the affirmative and he invited us in to the house. He told us he only used two rooms in the cottage: one contained a table and a couple of chairs, which had all seen better days, and there was an old mattress propped up against the wall which he used to drop onto the floor at night for his bed. He brought out a couple of glasses for us, and a tin mug for himself, and fetched a couple of bottles of mead. We duly drank his health. One glass led to another and we learnt that he was an oboe player. By this stage both Billy, my assistant, and I had begun to feel a little merry, so I suggested to him that it was time we headed for home, as we had a tractor and trailer outside. With half a mile of cart track before we reached the road it was going to take a bit of navigating, especially since there was an old chalk pit about 50 yards from the road. Billy volunteered to drive and I climbed into the back of the trailer. For most of the way all went well, but as we approached the pit I could see that Billy's head was beginning to nod so I gave him a shout to warn him about the pit – but it was too late! He turned his head when he heard me shout, and down the bank we went. Fortunately the tractor was only a small Ferguson so it didn't sink, and we were in the shallow end of the pit, although Billy did get his backside wet. Luckily for us one of the men was working on the field nearby cultivating so he came over with his tractor and pulled us out.

The next piece of news I got was the best I'd had for some time. My dear wife told me she was pregnant and that the new addition to our family should arrive in September (1964). This would work out just right as from the end of September until Christmas things usually quietened down for me with the sheep. Unfortunately it didn't work out that way this year. I received a letter from Mr Craigie, who farmed just outside Dublin. He had purchased a ram from us at the Society Sale last year and he was not very pleased with him after they had sheared him. I wrote back telling him I was sorry to hear that, but I offered him a little advice. Never buy a recently trimmed ram just because he looks nice – it's surprising what a pair of hand shears and a wire comb can do in the hands of an experienced shepherd. I told him that I didn't want him to think that I was trying to deceive him, but part of my job is to try to make an ordinary sheep look quite respectable, and I hoped that this bit of advice might be of some help to him and his shepherd.

I thought that would be the end of the affair, but not a bit of it. I received a letter back about a month before our baby was due. Mr Craigie asked me if I could come over to Dublin any time before the end of October to show his shepherd a few tricks of the trade. The trip was to be all expenses paid, plus full pay for as long as it took me. This put me in a bit of a quandary as the baby was due at the end of September. I wanted to get the trip to Ireland over and done with before the baby arrived; in those days your baby was born in the family home with a midwife in attendance. So I arranged to go across the Irish Sea for two days in the first week of October. My train and boat tickets arrived for 4th October, and I was keeping my fingers crossed that the baby would arrive a few days early or a day or two late. But it was not to be – our new son arrived on time, on 29th September 1964, a fine boy with no complications, and we named him Simon Patrick. The second name we chose was nothing to do with my trip to Ireland; well, not really. I told Pat that I didn't want to go and leave her so soon. Of course, she knew me better than that; her reply was that I would go whatever she said. So I promised I would only be away for two days.

The one part of the trip I was not relishing was the boat crossing across the Irish Sea. It brought back memories of my navy days. The sea and I did not always agree with each other, and I knew that the Irish Sea could be pretty rough. During the war when I was at sea, even the rattle of an anchor chain would start me heaving, so I was hoping it was going to be a smooth crossing. On arrival in Dublin I was met by Mr Craigie. We went straight to his farm and had a good look round the sheep, and then he took me to meet his parents. Of course, this being Ireland, the first thing you get offered is a glass of whisky, which was very tasty. I also met his shepherd. I told the shepherd that I wanted to get everything ready that afternoon so we could spend the next day trimming, which would give him a chance to see how it was done and time for him to have a go himself. I spent most of the next day showing him how the job was done and left the shepherd with a lamb that I had done a good job on. As I told him, the only way to get it right is with practice and more practice. I told Mr Craigie that I hoped I had passed on some of my knowledge, at least enough to get him started. I caught the night boat back to England, arriving home with my family the next day.

I must have made a good impression with what I had done over in the Emerald Isle as I received a letter from the Southern Ireland Suffolk Sheep Society, asking me if I could come over again next year for a few days and give a demonstration to the members of the society there.

1966 turned out to be a bit of a disaster towards the end of the year, even though the shows and sales were up to standard.

My second trip to Ireland was the next big event for me. I wrote and told Mr Craigie that I was coming over and that I wanted four sheep washed and dried for 15th October. I got a letter by return, with my fare only as this time I was to travel by air from Heathrow. I was quite excited about this as I had never been in an aeroplane before. It made me feel quite important.

Upon arrival I was met by Mr Craigie, and I was to stay with him for this visit. After the usual large whisky, Irish of course, and a very enjoyable meal, I thought to myself, this is not happening to me, but I guess I can put up with it.

The next morning I was driven to a large livestock market in Dublin where I was to give my demonstration. I was a bit nervous at first, then I began to get uneasy as there had been a lot of rain the day before. I was just hoping that the sheep would be dry, but I need not have worried – they had four ewe lambs in the ring and five 'good men and true' with hair dryers. By the time I had chatted to a lot of the Irish sheepmen and had a couple of Irish whiskies I was raring to go. It was a most enjoyable day; the only thing that puzzled them was how I could trim two or three sheep in half a day when their wives could only do one in a day. I suggested that maybe if they were to get hold of the carder and do a bit of combing themselves then the wives might be able to do a bit more trimming. The day ended with a good discussion and a question and answer session, and of course, another generous glass of Irish whisky, or Guinness, whatever was preferred.

Then they took my hat and passed it around for a collection, for my services. After that it was back to Mr Craigie's home for the night, and a good Irish meal. In the morning I was driven to the airport and before I knew it I was back at Heathrow and heading for home. It was good to be home with my wife and family again. Little did I know what I was to face in the coming weeks.

About ten days before lambing was due to start, I went out to work and the first thing I saw when I reached the sheep was a ewe standing on her own with a couple of lambs. I could see straight away that the lambs were dead. The thought goes through your head as to what was the cause of that, but it didn't worry me too much at the time, as you're lucky if you don't get the odd ewe keb (that's an old word for abort). However, a day or two later two more ewes did the same thing.

I solved the problem. In vet's language it was called toxoplasmosis. In my language it was blood poisoning of the placenta. By the end of February I had finished lambing, and in that time 50 ewes had aborted. Some I had managed to get lambs on, the rest would have nothing to do until next year. The vets advised me to keep all the female sheep together, including last year's ewe lambs which would be coming into the flock next year. Apparently they were hoping that with the tests they had taken, they were pretty sure that this type of abortion is self-immunising, especially since this was a closed flock – no females had ever been bought into the flock since it was formed in 1906, and hopefully never would be, and this proved quite true. I finished up with 140 lambs from 102 ewes, so with a little bit of luck I would have enough lambs to pick a show team from, and hopefully enough ram lambs for my regular customers.

In the meantime I had two young lads who wanted to learn about the sort of shepherding I was doing. The first lad came from Ireland. His name was Peter McCulloch and he was the son of one of the sheep farmers I had met when I was over in Ireland. The second lad had arrived later in the year and he was a waste of time. I can't even remember his name. The only thing I can remember about him was his car, and I wish I'd never seen him or his car. It was December and the time of the Smithfield Show, but with foot and mouth disease in East Anglia at the time, no livestock was allowed to go to the show. I think the lad's name was Tim;

I'll call him that for now anyway. He said he wanted to go and see what Smithfield was like, and he offered to take me with him in his car and pay for me to go in. In the end I told him I would go with him. We set off very early so as to miss the early traffic. We hadn't gone very far when I asked him to put the heater on, to which he replied that it didn't work. I said, 'Before we go any further, is there anything else in this car that doesn't work? Because if there is, you'd better turn round and take me back. In any case I don't fancy going through London in this old banger, so you had better make for Ongar and we'll catch the underground to Earl's Court.'

Eventually we arrived at the Show and had a look round. It was a big disappointment in more ways than one. Not only the lack of livestock, but I was also not looking forward to getting back in that car. So I suggested we leave early to get home before dark. Getting back to Ongar was no problem, but when he went to start his car it hadn't got a spark of life in it. Luckily there was a garage nearby, so Tim went and got a mechanic to come and get it started. Lifting the bonnet, the mechanic stood and just looked at it for a minute or two, and then he asked us how far we had to go. When I told him we had to go all the way to Suffolk, he said 'If I get the thing going, for goodness sake don't let it stop, or it will never start again.'

How true that was. Tim had to drive with the windows down because the windscreen wipers did not work so we had to keep leaning out and round to clean the windows. We managed to get within a mile or so from home and then the ruddy thing stopped. I have never been so cold in all my life. When I got out of the car I shook with cold. I told him that the best thing he could do was to take it to the scrap yard.

6

The flock moves to Badlingham

In the meantime Mr Dick told me that Lacey Scott had asked him whether he intended to keep the flock on. A wealthy client of Lacey Scott's had just bought a farm and they were looking for a flock of Suffolks. Mr Dick would rather see his sheep sold to a good home as a complete flock than see them all split up and never heard of again. I knew that his main interest was his herd of pedigree Landrace pigs, and he was honest enough to say that he didn't know much about the sheep, so we decided to go ahead and make some enquiries.

I found out about the mystery client – his name was R. L. Broad, and he had bought a farm on the Suffolk/Cambridge border, a 700-acre arable farm. He had a small herd of Hereford cattle and a herd of Landrace pigs. He was a top man in Lloyd's Insurance in London and was soon to retire. He spent the week in London, coming down to the farm at weekends. At this stage Mr Dick had been having discussions with the auctioneers. It was then arranged that Mr and Mrs Broad should come and see me and Patricia. Accordingly, they turned up on the Sunday morning in a posh Rolls Royce, introduced themselves and asked if I would be kind enough to show them the sheep. I was well prepared for this, as I had them on a fresh bit of grass just at the back of my house. We had a chat about the flock regarding its history and achievements. I could tell he didn't know much about sheep, if anything, but he was very impressed with what he

The thatched cottage in which the Riggalls lived whilst at Badlingham

saw. I could tell he was a gentleman of top class and Mrs Broad struck me as a country lover, nothing snooty or townie about her whatsoever. So far, so good, I thought, as they left. Mr Broad said he would be in touch with Lacey Scott and if they came to an agreement then he would get in touch with me. Next weekend, true to his word, the Rolls pulled up at my gate. This time he was on his own. He told me that he had agreed to buy the flock if I would come and be shepherd for him. Failing that, he would not buy them. I told him I would give him my answer when my wife and I had been and seen the place.

'Well, when can you come? No time like the present!'

It was only ten miles away, so off we went. As we got nearer to the farm he told us that the only problem he had at the moment was that he had nowhere for us to live, but that he could sort something out. We pulled up outside a very attractive thatched cottage, and like all the other cottages it was painted Suffolk pink. All the houses were occupied by men who were working on the farm, including the farm manager. A public road ran through the centre of the farm, leading to Chippenham. The grass verges were mown like a lawn, with white stakes driven in to stop vehicles running onto the grass. You would have to see it to believe it. I was then informed that the thatched cottage was where we were to live if I decided to take the job, but at that moment in time Mr Broad and his wife were living in it while the farmhouse was being renovated. We had a look round the farm buildings, which to say the least were more like the National Stud than a farmyard. The main yard was all concrete with tubular steel cattle pens and mahogany doors which were held together with brass screws. The sheep shed was made in the same way. I was then asked if I would take the job. I conferred with Patricia and we agreed that if the sheep were coming here then so were we. I told Mr Broad that I'd take his job so long as we didn't have to wait too long before we moved.

With that he drove us back to Lackford. It was the end of an unbelievable day. Mr Broad said he would let us know as soon as possible regarding the move. We didn't have to wait too long for his reply. He said that his wife had suggested that they should move out of the thatched cottage and go and stay in the Worthington Hotel in the next village, so that we could move in within the week, or as soon as was convenient. Mrs Broad, or Dodo as she liked to be called, took charge of things. First, she asked me if I could drive.

I replied no, the only thing I'd ever driven was a tractor and a bike.

'Well, that won't do. There's a Land Rover there doing nothing.' So she said I could use that for my work and for my own use as well, and she would book me in for driving lessons. She also offered to take me out and give me a chance to get used to driving. Life was getting better every day.

I don't think the farm manager thought much of me as I was only answerable to Mr Broad. I was to find out later that the manager didn't know much about livestock at all. We weren't long before we crossed swords. Prior to moving I had always sold the fat lambs and cull ewes in

Simpson's market at Bury, where the market foreman and I got on very well. I could always rely on Bunny (that was his nickname as he didn't like his full name, Bernard). I had the privilege of taking my sheep in the night before the sale, and Bunny would put them in the right pens for me in the morning. I asked him if I could keep the same arrangement when I moved and he said that it wouldn't be a problem.

After I had got the sheep settled into their new home at Mr Broad's, I had half a dozen old ewes to cull and I told Mr Broad that I would enter them in Simpson's Market. He said to do what I thought best. The following week I rang Bunny and told him the farm manager would be bringing them in as I had not passed my driving test yet. I loaded the sheep into the trailer and told him where to take them. I never thought any more about it until I saw Bunny at the weekend and the first thing he said was what happened to the sheep. I said I had sent them in with the manager.

Well, the mystery was solved the next day; instead of taking the sheep where I had told him to, he had taken them to Lacey Scott's market. I went after that farm manager and I let rip good and proper. I think I can honestly say that it was the only time in my whole working life that I ever swore or lost my temper with anyone. And to make matters worse, Mr Broad came along at that moment, and asked what was wrong, and I wasn't long in telling him. He told me to calm down and he took me up to the office and gave me a gin and tonic and a cigar. It was not quite the start to the new job I would have liked.

This was going to be the first time in my shepherding career that I was to have lamb yard with a roof over it and electric lights, and all only a few steps from my back door. It was going to be quite a change, after being out in a field all night in a wooden hut with a straw yard and a Tilley lantern for the past 15 years. As well as having the barn to lamb in, I had a straw yard out in the field where the kale and swedes were. The ewes and lambs were taken there once they were two or three weeks old. They could go out and come back in as they liked, but they were shut in at night. The ewes had hay and the lambs had a creep that the ewes could not get to, as the lambs had *ad lib* trough feed. I remember Mrs Broad coming to have a look round one afternoon as she had never seen anything like this before. She remarked on how cosy they all looked, and then she came out with a few words that made me smile.

'They look a little bored. Do you think they would like some music?'

I replied that I hadn't heard of that before, and that I was afraid the gamekeeper wouldn't think much of that as it would probably scare the pheasants away.

When I met her in the farmyard a day or two later she had just been talking to Mr Macdonald, the vet. She called me over to introduce me but I told her I already knew him as it was the same vet that used to come to Lackford. A few days later I saw the vet on the farm again and being a bit curious I sort of accidentally on purpose bumped into him and in the course of our conversation I asked him what brought him here so often. He replied that he had to keep an eye on the cattle, a small herd of Herefords. There had been problems with the calving as the man who looked after them knew very little about them and they were getting more dead calves than live ones. Apparently the fellow who was responsible admitted that he didn't know the first thing about the job. I could not believe what I was hearing and I had a chat with the stockman. He had worked on the farm as a general farm worker before it had changed hands and he was told he could stay and work for the new owners if he wished. To my amazement he told me that when the cattle arrived on the farm he was detailed to look after them. He said he didn't know anything about cattle breeding but he always did as he was told, meaning what the farm manager told him. Dodo came round the farm next morning with her dogs for a walk, and to check that the men's room was clean and the supply of tea and coffee was adequate.

We always had a chat about the farm and things in general; the topic this morning was about the cattle; things were not going according to plan and the vets' bills were far too high. In the course of the conversation I jokingly said it would be cheaper to build a house and let the vet live here. She looked at me, she didn't know if I was being serious or not. I told her I was only pulling her leg. She asked me what I thought was wrong. I said that the problem was that the two people looking after them at the moment knew nothing about breeding cattle and that the sooner they got an experienced stockman the better it would be for them. I told her they had some good cows in the herd but it needed someone with a bit of experience to look after them. She must have taken a bit of notice of what I said as there was an advert in the *Farmers' Weekly* the following week. Three men applied for the job but only one was really interested, so with no opposition he got the job. At least things began to improve in the cattle yards.

At this time Mr Broad was still in business with Lloyd's Insurance in London so I only got to see him at weekends. He travelled around the world quite a bit, which accounted for several export orders over the next few years to France, Belgium, Holland, Germany, Italy, Spain, Norway, India and South America. The main lot of rams were sold locally at Bury St Edmunds sheep sales, depending on what the trade was like. Sometimes we went to Northampton and Leicester. I remember on one occasion I was asked to get a ram ready for a big charity sale in aid of cancer research to be held in Tattersall's sale ring. The sale was to take place one evening along with foals, paintings and many more valuable items. The buyers were mainly farmers and the horsey fraternity, plus a few dealers interested in works of art. I had to parade the sheep round the ring as if it were a racehorse. It was eventually knocked down for £350 to Mr Vestey who farmed a large estate just outside town.

By now we had settled into the thatched cottage. Compared to other houses we had lived in it was real luxury: the floors were all carpeted except for the kitchen which had red quarry tiles which the children used to keep polished with dusters on their hands and feet. It was the biggest room in the house with a large Aga cooker which was very handy for warming your backside against and it kept the house very cosy! As Patricia spent a lot of time alone, she did most of the gardening, so Dodo asked her if she would like a greenhouse. She didn't need asking twice. The next day a nice sized greenhouse arrived and was erected. I thought I would try my hand at growing some chrysanthemums in it, the large single blooms you see at flower shows. I remember my father used to grow them, but it proved to be an expert's job and I hadn't got the time to spend on them. It was a case of shepherds look after sheep and gardeners look after flowers. Patricia had a nice bed of strawberries just under the bedroom window and she woke me up one morning saying that it sounded as if we had got some pigs in the garden as she could hear snorting and grunting. She jumped out of bed to discover a family of hedgehogs having an early breakfast of our strawberries. Naturally they had eaten all the ripe ones so it was goodbye to strawberries and cream for tea that day. To make sure it didn't happen again I had to put some netting over them.

Showing season was around again and I was asked to support the one-day shows – Hertfordshire, Cambridge and Isle of Ely – which I didn't mind as it was good training for the sheep, getting them to lead and show themselves off. There is nothing worse than taking a sheep into a judging ring and you can't lead it or show it at its best.

Peterborough Show Champion 1989

Champion Suffolk female:
with the Duchess of Kent, 1968

I shall always remember winning my first Royal Show championship. I had won the class for the shearling ram purely because the ram that was second on the day would not lead. The judge couldn't make up his mind until he asked me to walk the sheep round. I was standing second at the time. Then he asked Harry, the shepherd to the Lawshall flock, to walk his sheep, which was standing first in the line-up. First his ram would not budge. He stuck his toes in and was determined he wasn't going anywhere. I was keeping my fingers crossed, hoping that my ram wasn't going to let me down. After several attempts Harry gave up, then the judge told me to try my luck. Well, the ram must have heard me telling him what I would do to him if he let me down. I'd told him I'd have his balls for breakfast! I knew he could do it but there's no telling what will happen on days such as this.

Here goes, I thought. And he strode across the ring like a sheep who knew he was going to win – and he did: the judge drew me up to first place and gave me the champion rosette. I literally threw my hat up into the air – it had taken me 20 years to do this but it had been worth the wait.

By now I had passed my driving test which made life easier. I could now drive myself to the shows and sales, which was a lot better than having to wait for someone else to take me. Plus the fact that I could take Patricia and the family out, and not have to wait for a bus.

This was the last year the National Suffolk Sheep Sale was to be held in Ipswich market. The Suffolk flocks in East Anglia were getting a bit thin on the ground, and the big money was being made in Northern Ireland and Scotland. It was decided that the National Sale would in future be held at the Royal Showground in Stoneleigh. I entered six lambs for the final Ipswich sale. This would be the last time we would see our friends from the Midlands and Northern England and the one or two breeders who used to come over from Wales. It literally killed off the sale of top breeders' rams in our area.

It also turned out to be a sad occasion. Ted Haggett, an old shepherd friend of mine from Yorkshire, was shepherd to Mr Putman from Gransmoor. Like most of the shepherds and their sheep, we used to arrive the day before the sale as we had to have an inspection. If any rams did not pass the inspection they had to be removed from the sale. It also meant that any of the shepherds and lorry drivers there had to sleep in the backs of their lorries and trailers. After the sheep had been settled down for the night we used to go into town for a high supper and a pint or two.

I'll tell you a little about Ted, who was a real Yorkshire character. I first met him at the Royal Show in Blackpool in 1953. There was no mistaking him once you had met him: a broad Yorkshire accent and a pair of Wellington boots cut off just above the ankle, which I'm sure he never removed. He was a jovial old boy and I'd never seen him out of colour with anyone. Anyway, we all got down in our lorries and trailers for the night, and with a full belly and a pint or two of beer we didn't want a lot of rocking. The first one up in the morning used to put the kettle on and make the tea. It just so happened that on that particular morning it fell to me, so I got busy and made the morning brew, a mug of tea all round and the morning wake-up call. I left Ted till last as he was known as a bit of a heavy sleeper. Derick, Ted's assistant, had been round the sheep just to check they were all alive and well, as he passed my trailer he shouted 'Is the kettle on? Don't forget Ted!'

I got another mug and took it to Ted's wagon. I called to him that I had his mug of tea and that I would bring it in – no reply.

I knocked on the wagon – still no reply. So I went up the tailboard of his trailer and there he was under his blanket. I bent down to wake him up and got the shock of my life. He was stone cold; he had died in his sleep. I went back to my trailer and Derick was there drinking his tea.

'Ted won't want his tea this morning mate, he's had his last drink. He's dead.'

It was a sad loss to all who knew him and it put a damper on the sale. But life had to go on.

I told RLB (that's Mr Broad, but I shall refer to him as RLB in future as it sounds a bit more friendly) that we needed a new ram if we were to keep in the top bracket of the shows and sales that we entered. He agreed with me and I was pleasantly surprised when he suggested we should go up to the sale in Edinburgh. We would have to go up the day before and spend the night there. He contacted the auctioneers and they arranged everything. I think someone had given them a tip-off that RLB was a wealthy man and a first-time buyer. We took a taxi to complete our journey to the sale yard, where RLB was greeted by the head man of the auctioneers in a bowler hat, who ushered him into his office. I saw the gin bottle on the table along with a box of cigars. I smiled to myself, thinking 'Bribery!', so I excused myself, telling RLB that I was going to have a look around the sheep.

RLB joined me later. He liked people to think he knew a bit about the task in hand. I knew which ram I wanted, but the last thing you want is the vendors to see how interested you are. I knew all about the particular ram as I had seen it out at the Royal Show, where it had won the championship. Anyhow, the sale got underway and the ring was packed. We sat up at the back. Eventually the ram entered the ring and you could tell right away that this sheep was going to make a lot of money. I told RLB not to start bidding until I told him to. The opening bid was 500 guineas and within a matter of minutes it was up to 1,500 guineas. I told RLB to start his bid. He was really enjoying his first attempt at buying a sheep and he was waving his catalogue about excitedly. As soon as they saw this it wasn't long before the price had topped 2,000 guineas, which for the early 1970s was a lot of money. I told him to put the book down and just nod his head. He did as I told him but he was determined to have the ram. Eventually it was knocked down to him for 2,500 guineas, a world record price at that time, but I'm sorry to say that the record was broken a bit later on. Still, RLB had enjoyed himself and I had the ram I wanted.

The next thing I was looking forward to was the arrival of our new baby on 6th September. The only difference this time was that whereas our other children had been born at home, Charles in Essex and Wendy and Simon in Suffolk, for medical reasons Patricia had to go into a nursing home in Ely, Cambridgeshire. Fortunately all went well and we had a fine healthy son, Duncan.

By now it was sale time again. The ram sales always came in September and early October, and the final one of the year was the Smithfield Fat Stock Show at Earl's Court in London, which lasts for about a week. RLB told me he would take me out to his club for an evening meal if I got a first prize, and that's just what I did. I won first prize for a pen of three butcher's lambs. RLB kept his word and told me to be outside Earl's Court main entrance at 7 o'clock that evening. It was a good job I'd brought a suit with me, or there would have been some funny looks if I'd walked into a gentlemen's club in my showing outfit. I don't somehow think they would have let me in, as I got some funny looks as it was.

Christmas was just around the corner and there was another surprise in store. All the family were invited to a Christmas party at the Rutland Arms in Newmarket; all the families of the men who worked on the farm were invited, and to top the festive season Dodo came round on Christmas Eve with a large turkey and a bottle of the best port.

A nice pen of Suffolk's being admired

7

Travels

With the coming of the New Year there was a good crop of lambs and another surprise. The British Livestock Exporters had contacted the Suffolk Sheep Society as they wanted six ewe lambs for the British trade stand at the Paris Agricultural Show. The Show reaches most of Europe and goes on for about eight days. RLB didn't want asking twice – he spoke quite good French and he had several business contacts in Paris. I had already got to know Monsieur Colombet who was responsible for importing Suffolk Sheep into France, and he asked RLB to bring me over to Paris as there would be a lot of information that the French breeders would want. He would be there to act as interpreter; it would not be much good if you couldn't speak French and didn't know what they were talking about.

It was all arranged that the sheep would be collected from the farm a day or two before the show, along with enough feed for them for the first few days – that was to make sure that a sudden change of diet didn't upset their stomachs. Everything went according to plan, and RLB and I set off the next day, travelling by train and ferry. I had no idea where I was going to stay, but it wasn't long before I found out. After a short train journey from Calais to Paris, a taxi dropped us outside the Hotel Maurice, a very posh place. I later learnt that it had been the German headquarters in Paris during the war. The following morning, all bright-eyed and bushy-tailed, we got a taxi to the Show. I was very impressed with what I saw – except for the sheep. I was glad I had trimmed our sheep and that they had travelled well, as they were creating quite a stir. They were the only sheep that had been trimmed and they were to be auctioned off after the Show. We could not take them home again unless they spent six months in quarantine, and as we had only planned to stay at the Show for three days it wasn't much good putting a reserve on them. We had another 24 hours at the Show then we flew back to Heathrow and home again. I can't say that I didn't enjoy myself, but it would have been much better if everybody spoke the same language.

While I had been away a young man had come to see me to ask if he could come and work with me to learn the secrets of shepherding, as he was hoping to go to the Royal Agricultural College at Cirencester. I asked RLB about it and he agreed to let him come with me for six months. And so Andrew Foulds joined the staff at Badlingham. He didn't live far away so there were no problems as regards accommodation. He more or less became part of our family, and he was a big help to me during his short spell with us.

I shall always remember him for an amusing incident when shearing time came round. I had always done my own shearing and Andrew asked if he could have a go. I said yes, but told him he would have to wait until I'd got to the last few in case anything went wrong. We got down to the last two ewes, then I told him he could have a go. Well, let's just say that he got the wool off without spilling too much blood, but shearing is like any other job: practice makes perfect. The following day he asked me if he could borrow my shearing machine as he had bought six ewes of his own and since they hadn't been shown it would be a good chance for him to learn a bit more about shearing. I thought it couldn't do much harm and so I let him take the shearing machine home. He was going to clip his sheep on the Sunday.

I had just finished my breakfast that Sunday when the phone rang. It was Andrew. He couldn't get the machine to cut and could I go over and put him right?

I got into the Land Rover and it took me about 20 minutes to find him. When I eventually found him I couldn't help but have a good laugh. He had two old boys off a nearby farm to help him and they just stood there laughing their heads off. Andrew was on his knees, sweating and swearing – not the sort of thing you would expect from the son of a parson. Wool was all over the place, there was more wool left on the sheep than he had taken off, and the only reason the machine wasn't cutting was because he hadn't adjusted the blades correctly. I think that was the last time Andrew ever attempted sheep shearing.

It was about this time when Patricia and I had been to see the village vicar about christening Duncan. The vicar was a miserable old so-and-so and told us he couldn't christen our son as we were not regular church-goers. Andrew came to the rescue and said he would ask his father if he could do it for us. He said he would be only too pleased to help and the christening took place the following Sunday at Littleport church. Dodo and RLB attended the service, which we thought was very nice of them. Duncan was the first newborn baby on the farm since they had bought it. I must have set a trend or perhaps it was something in the water, as the next three new employees' wives produced seven children between them in the space of six or seven years.

By this time Charles, our eldest son, had left school and was training to be a baker. He had no interest in sheep and I can't blame him for that. I can't visualise any shepherd's son in this area taking over from his father. The hours at work are too long, and unless wages rise a lot I cannot see that in ten years' time there will be any large show flocks about which require a full-time shepherd. And if you wanted one I doubt you would be able to find one.

Forty years ago I was the youngest shepherd in East Anglia, as far as Suffolk sheep flocks were concerned; not that that was the way I had planned it. I was dropped in at the deep end and took a chance that I might make a go of it. And here I am 40 years later, and I think I'm now the only full-time shepherd with a large show flock in the Eastern Counties.

While on the subject of children and getting back to Duncan, he was a big baby weighing in at 11lb. Unfortunately Patricia was unable to breastfeed him for medical reasons, and that probably saved our lives.

Living in a thatched cottage meant that the interior was made up of old wooden beams and plaster; the main beam supported the chimney, and the Aga cooker was underneath. For some unknown reason Duncan woke up early for his bottle. Normally he never woke before 6 a.m., but on this particular morning he was yelling for his feed at 5.15 a.m. Being the good father, I told Pat I would go downstairs and get him his bottle. Half-way down the stairs I could smell smoke – I knew something was wrong. Opening the door at the foot of the stairs I was met by a roar of flames which were coming out into the kitchen from under the large wooden beam over the Aga. The first thing I did was to grab the phone and dial 999 for the fire brigade. Then I dashed upstairs and told Patricia what was happening. At first she though I was having her on, then she realised I was serious. I got the children up, but by now they were up and dressed as they guessed there was something wrong. It wasn't long before we heard the fire engine bell. They apologized for not getting to us sooner, but when they ran out of houses in Chippenham village they turned round and went back as they thought they were on the wrong road. Fortunately, George Smally the village baker was having an early bake and he directed them to us. Another blessing was the fact that the gentleman who lived next to the farm had a moat around his house, so the firemen had an ample supply of water. It was not very long before they had the flames out, then they had to cut the old beam out to find out what had caused the fire. It appeared that the metal flue that went up the centre of the chimney had rusted, allowing hot soot to fall down on top of the wooden beam. It could have been smouldering for weeks. The fireman told us it was a good job I had got up early as the flames had burnt through the airing cupboard and were scorching the floor of Wendy's bedroom. Another 15 minutes and it would have been a very different story. I shall always be grateful to the Newmarket Fire Brigade for doing such a good job.

While this was going on, Dodo had come down when she heard the fire engine and she had taken Patricia and the children up to the farmhouse. They didn't have to stay there too long as there wasn't much damage done – the firemen had done a brilliant job and by the time they left you could hardly see where they had been. I gave the all clear to Patricia to ask Dodo to bring her home again, just in time for breakfast. The gods must have been smiling on us at this time because if it had happened a week later I would have been at the Smithfield Show in Earl's Court. I dread to think of that. And to make matters even worse for Patricia, earlier in the year the house had been found to be full of woodworm, and the pest control people turned up without warning when I was away, and took up carpets and fumigated the roof from the inside. The best thing to come out of that was the amount of queen wasps we found dead outside in the garden. They must have been hibernating in the thatch.

Before we knew it, it was lambing time again, and with no problems. Having a nice warm barn just outside your back door makes the job so much easier. Then it was off to Paris again, only this time we were going to fly. And this time they had been told that they had to pay for the sheep before they left the farm. I had been asked to give a trimming demonstration on the second day. I was really looking forward to that as long as there was an interpreter standing by. It was early March when the sheep were transported to the Paris Show, and we flew out from Heathrow two days later. It didn't seem very long after take-off that we were looking down over the French coast, and I'm convinced that it's the only way to travel. On arrival at the hotel RLB suggested that we have a drink or two then go out for a meal later. That turned out to be a meal I shall not forget in a hurry. He told me we were going to a fish restaurant. Of course, I thought that this would be just a posh fish and chip shop. How wrong I was. A friend of his had booked a table for the three for us, but worse was to come.

The waiter came round with the menu which was mostly written in French which I couldn't read. Anyhow, RLB asked me what I would like. I thought that the best way out of this would to be to say I'll have the same as you. Well, the first course was a plate with six large oysters. I had never before seen the inside of an oyster, let alone eat one. What was I to do? I couldn't say I didn't like them because I'd never eaten them before, so, filling my wine glass, I swallowed them all very quickly. The rest of the meal was much better, a fish dish of some sort, but by then my stomach had begun to tell me that it didn't like oysters. I felt as sick as a pig. RLB's friend could see I was feeling a bit queasy and without saying anything he passed me some dry toast and a cup of coffee. This settled my raging stomach and I haven't looked at oysters from that day to this.

The trimming demonstration at the show created quite a lot of interest, during which time I was approached by a chap on the British Livestock trade stand who wanted to know if I would be interested in managing a flock in the South of France. I told him that at that moment in time that would be the last thing I'd want.

RLB told me he would be staying one more night so I would have to go home on my own. I was quite pleased with this idea. He rang up and ordered a taxi to take me to the airport. As I walked out of the hotel to get into my taxi there was quite a commotion behind me. The Head Waiter came and one of his helpers caught up with me and told me that I couldn't go as I had not paid my bill. It was a good job they could speak English as I had to go back into the hotel and explain that I was Mr Broad's shepherd and that he was going to pay. After a phone call to RLB's room the Head Waiter was all smiles and apologies, and so I left Paris probably for the last time.

1972 came and went. By now the show circuit was getting bigger and slowly improving, as far as awards were concerned. Another trip to Scotland was planned for August. I was to drive up in the Land Rover and RLB was going to fly up and meet me there. The next day all went well. We purchased another ram from the Barrons flock. RLB decided he would drive home as he thought he knew the way better than I did. I was only too pleased at that time to let him drive. But then he told me we would go back over the Cheviot Hills via Penrith. Eventually we arrived at a hotel a few miles from the A1 and then he decided to stay the night as it was getting late.

'That's OK with me. But what about the ram in the back?' I asked him. So RLB went to see the proprietor. As it was a country hotel there were some outbuildings nearby, and so we unloaded the ram and gave him a bucketful of water and some hay. Then a good meal was served up for us and I was soon asleep. The next morning RLB had changed his mind and said I had better drive the rest of the way home. I heaved a sigh of relief. He slept most of the way home.

In the meantime a fresh pigman had been taken on, the last one having moved on to pastures new. This new man wasn't very popular with the rest of the men; the only friend he seemed to have was the farm manager. It was a breeding herd of pigs and the pigs were on points, I think the organisation in those days was called the PIDA. Most of the stock was sold over the telephone, which leads me on to a very funny story.

The pigman rang me to ask whether I was using the trailer as they had sold a boar to a farmer in Cromer, North Norfolk and had to deliver him. I told him I wouldn't be needing the trailer over the next few days. Then I heard that RLB would be going with him. Well, the pig was duly loaded. They called in at the garage en route to top up with fuel and away they went, arriving in Cromer some hours later. On dropping the tail gate, no pig! Apparently they had not checked the small door at the front of the trailer and when they took a right hand turn about 400 yards from the farm, the pig had fallen out and the door had slammed shut again. To make the whole thing more laughable, the pig had arrived back at the farm before they got back, and was waiting for them!

The mid-1970s was a period of mixed events, some good and some not so good. After spending quite a lot of money on rams at the Edinburgh Sale over the past years, two of my shepherd friends decided to take some rams up to the Edinburgh Sale to sell, and see if we could get some of our money back. The plan was to travel up by lorry to Berwick and stop overnight at a farm owned by a Mr Islop. We would unload the sheep, spend the night there then go to the sale. The idea seemed all right until the time came to load up, when we found out we couldn't all fit in to the cab of the lorry. So being as I was the youngest, I had to travel in the back with the sheep. It was not a journey I would recommend, and to make matters worse, we didn't sell a single sheep.

The author waits while his show sheep are loaded into a trailer

Mr Broad informed me that he had been elected president of the Suffolk Sheep Society and that he had been asked to judge the national flock competition. I couldn't see how he was going to do this as his knowledge of sheep was not very good, to say the least. But a phone call from a friend sorted things out. John Cook, the son of a well known Suffolk breeder in Oxfordshire, was to be his assistant and driver. John was on the official judges' list, so I guessed he would be doing the judging.

As for our own results on the show circuit over the season, it was fantastic: Supreme Champion and Reserve Supreme Champion at the Royal Show in 1973. What a celebration we had that night! I woke up the next morning under the lorry that we were using as our living quarters, and not in the lorry. I cannot remember much about anything after falling down the tailboard in an attempt to get back to my trailer, where I should have slept the night.

Prior to that I had won the Supreme Champion at the Suffolk Show, the Royal Norfolk Show and the East of England Show. This was to be the best showing spell of my career. I had become the one to beat in East Anglia. As far as the judging at the Royal Show was concerned, it was now becoming a case of you scratch my back and I'll scratch yours.

Our friends from north of the border began to drift down to Stoneleigh and the old shepherds used to say that they brought their judge with them. It happened to me on one occasion. I was standing second in a class of shearling ewes. The judge, a gentleman from the North, put me up to first position, and I thought he agreed with so many other people around the ring that this was a good ewe, who had not been beaten at four shows that season prior to coming to the Royal. But standing next to me in second place was a ewe from over the border, and it was no more than I expected when the judge walked along the line and then swapped the first and second ewes round. I was quite annoyed at this move, and I made the decision there and then that this was to be our last Royal Show. I would not have minded if it had been a difficult decision for the judge to make, but this had been so obvious that it even brought comments from the spectators around the ring.

The next occasion worth mentioning was the flood in the autumn of 1975. The ewes were heavy in lamb and running in a meadow alongside the river Kennett. I wouldn't really call it a river, it was more of a small stream. On this occasion it had been raining for two or three days. I had been down to the ewes in the morning to see if they were all on four legs; the stream was in full flow but no higher than I had seen it before.

Anyhow, a knock came on my back door when I was having my lunch. It was the farm foreman, David Kinsey, to tell me that I had better go down to the meadow as there was a lot of water coming downriver and it was still rising. We jumped into the Land Rover and sped off as fast as we could. On arrival at the field I could see things were getting serious. The gate was at the highest point of the meadow, which sloped downhill, and water was flooding the meadow, driving the sheep down to a dead end from where they would not be able to escape. We had to do something pretty quickly or they would all drown.

David sped off back to the farm to get help and I told him to bring some wire cutters back with him. The only way out was across the stream on to a neighbour's farm. What we had to do was find the narrowest spot and make a human chain to pass the ewes across the stream. The ewes were too frightened to go too far away from the gap we had made in the wire fence as long as the water didn't rise too quickly. Hopefully this would work. Two men were on the bank on our side catching the sheep and pushing them into the water. There were three men in the stream and two more men on the other side. Once we had got a few sheep onto the other side of the river all went well. The ewes saw their mates and dry land. We pushed the stubborn sheep into the water and the ewes still waiting in the floodwater began to jump in by themselves. And you hear people say that sheep have no brains! Eventually we managed to get them all across, 150 in-lamb ewes. It was some feat, I know, even though we had lost some ewes. Our neighbours were very helpful and let the sheep stay in their barn overnight. We moved them back to the farm the next day. I had a count up, and remarkably we had only lost five ewes, and not one aborted either. I dread to think what would have happened if that flood had happened during the night.

I suppose I should have mentioned this before, but as the next five months passed in the usual routine, I should like to mention now a few friends who have called on me for advice and help.

First, I would just like to mention our new vicar; the miserable old

*Winning ewe lambs Eastern Area flock competition
at Hall Farm, Fornham St Martin
organised by the Suffolk Sheep Society*

so-and-so who had refused to christen our youngest son suddenly left the parish and was replaced by a very nice young man. I came home from work one day and he was sitting in the kitchen having a cup of tea and a chat with Patricia. He was a very pleasant chap and he never mentioned the Almighty once. When he fancied a good cuppa and a chat he knew where to come. I got the feeling he was building up to something, and as the end of the year approached I found out I hadn't been wrong. He called in one day and asked for me; I thought to myself, here it comes. 'I know you're a shepherd and don't have time to go to church very often, especially at Christmas time, but I would very much like you to come and read the lesson at the Christmas Service.' I was quite taken aback. The only times I had been to church in recent years was for christenings, weddings and funerals.

Then there was Dick Abbott. By profession Dick was a picture framer and his wife was a historian who tutored at Cambridge. Apparently he had been on holiday in the Lake District and he had returned home with half a dozen sheep. The only thing was, he didn't know much about them so he had been told to ring me. Dick lived in Burwell, near Newmarket, in what looked like a converted chapel, with a bit of grass out the back which I suppose he was hoping he could feed his sheep on. Anyhow, I had a ride over to see him. He was quite surprised when I told him what was involved with sheep keeping: drenching, injecting, shearing etc. He asked me to let him know when these things wanted doing, then he asked me in to the house to have a drink. I found out that even if he didn't know much about sheep, he certainly could make a very good home brew. I told him to keep in touch if he had any problems.

The only thing wrong with doing little jobs in your spare time is that word gets around and the phone never stops ringing – if it's not one thing it's another. Most of the calls I got were asking me if I knew of anyone who could shear a few sheep; what they were really asking is whether I could do it for them. It was mostly people who keep five or six sheep, lawnmowers I call them. I suppose the reason for this is that the shearing gangs that go round don't really want to do anything with small lots of sheep. I didn't mind helping because people were so glad to get them done that they always paid well over the normal rate.

I got a call once from the owner of a racehorse stud in the next village,

Worlington. He asked if I could come and shear one sheep. It was only two miles away, so off I went. When I arrived they got the sheep out of the stable, which also contained a very smart racehorse. Usually horses will give sheep a good kick, or bite them if they get anywhere near them, but in this case the horse would not settle without the sheep being there. Mind you, that racehorse did quite a bit of snorting and prancing around when his sheep went back into the stable without its wool.

I think of everything I did this was the most interesting. I got a phone call one evening from a lady who said she was ringing on behalf of a Miss Bartholomew, who lived in Stetchworth, a village near Newmarket. She asked whether I knew anyone who could shear some sheep for her. When I asked how many there were, she replied that she didn't really know, so I told her I would be along at the weekend to have a look. I decided to go there on Sunday ('better the day, better the deed' so they say). On arriving at what used to be a stud in the centre of the horse-racing community, I was met by several dogs who didn't seem very friendly.

Anyhow, after a few minutes a lady came to see what they were barking at. She struck me as someone who didn't mind what she looked like when working with her livestock. She was dressed in an old coat tied round the waist with a bit of cord and old wellies on her feet. She introduced herself as Miss Bartholomew, and I had a funny feeling that this was going to be something a bit different. She let me into the yard. The first thing I wanted to see were the sheep, so Miss B. (as I used to call her) picked up an empty bucket, walked over to the field adjoining the yard, rattled it and gave a couple of calls. Lo and behold, a flock of four-horned Jacob sheep arrived from all directions and to this day I cannot remember how many there were. I arranged to come and shear them the following weekend. Having got that sorted out we had a walk around. The horseboxes were now being used for other purposes. Some were still being used as retirement homes for elderly racehorses, and one contained rather a lot of guinea-pigs. There were chickens all over the place and a small herd of Jersey cows which were machine-milked by Miss B.

A Jacob sheep

It was, to put it mildly, an animal paradise. They were all well fed. The chickens laid their eggs just wherever they liked. And I mustn't forget to mention the cats. There were several of them and they had a room in the house all to themselves.

Shearing day arrived. Accompanied by Patricia, we made a start. All went well until I caught a ewe and found she only had one back leg. On enquiring what had happened, Miss B. told me that it had broken the other one about two years before and rather than have the ewe destroyed she'd had the leg amputated, and it was still able to have lambs. It was a good job the old Jacob ram wasn't too heavy, though as the old saying goes, where there's a will, there's a way. Eventually I got to the last sheep, and then Miss B. said, 'I have one more that I keep in the house.'

I thought she was joking, but she disappeared and returned a few minutes later carrying an old ewe. She laid it on the shearing board, and told us that the sheep was very old and that it had had a stroke, and would I be very, very careful with her as no one else had sheared her since she had been afflicted. Miss B. said that in the past she had cut the

Shearing a Jacob ('Mind the horns!') ram

wool off by herself with a large pair of scissors. I was as gentle as I could be. Having got the wool off, the old ewe didn't seem any the worse for it. Miss B. asked me to carry the old ewe back into the house and she led the way as I hadn't been into the house before. We went straight through the living room into a large unfurnished room; there was a bed on the floor where the old sheep lived, but what amazed us was how clean it all was. A good cup of tea was the next thing, before Pat and I left for home. I promised to keep in touch and told her she could phone me if she needed any help. There was certainly plenty to talk about on the way home.

8

Troubles

The show season came and went with a good number of awards, and with the sales approaching RLB asked me if I wanted a ram this time round. I said that I had only seen one that I was interested in but it would mean a trip up to Edinburgh. He replied that that would be all right as he was going up for a holiday to Gleneagles the same week as the sale. He told me there would therefore be no need for me to go as he would go to the sale on his own while he was up there. I was a bit worried about this, but I thought that if I gave him the name of the breeder and the lot number of the ram with strict instructions not to buy anything else, then he should be all right; this was how it was arranged. Then he would give me a ring to let me know how the ram would be getting home. That seemed pretty straightforward and that was how we left it.

Nothing more was said about it but I got a little worried as the day of the sale approached. If those crafty old Scots got to know that RLB was after a certain sheep, they would get together and run the price up, but they actually did more than that. I got a phone call from him that evening to say that he had not been able to buy the ram I had asked him to buy as he thought it was going to make too much money and so he had stopped bidding at 300 guineas. But he had bought three other rams, and they would be at Peterborough railway station at 2 o'clock the following morning and I was to collect them. The ram I had asked for had been sold for 750 guineas. He had paid twice as much for these three, and he couldn't even remember the names of the breeders he had bought them from. Well, Pat and I set off for Peterborough station just after 8 p.m. I was not looking forward to this trip and, to make matters worse, just as we arrived at the station there was one hell of a clap of thunder and we had to sit in the cab until the storm was over. Then the train was late. When it did eventually arrive I went over to see where the sheep were. I found a porter pushing them in a cage on a trolley along the platform. I didn't even bother to look at the animals. We transferred them into the trailer and made for home. In the morning I went to see what the rams really looked like in daylight, and I was not a happy shepherd.

My breeding policy over the years has always been when you see a ram you like you go for it and try and buy it the year before you want it. It gives you the chance to see if he can work all right by running him with two or three old ewes. It's also a good idea to have him tested before you put him to work properly. It was also my policy that if he left the type of lamb you were looking for, then I would pick out a good son of his and keep that. I found that during my years with lamb flocks it helped to keep uniformity in the ewes.

I turned the rams out on a paddock and I didn't like what I saw any more than when I had seen them in the shed. I now had to think what I was going to say to RLB when he got back from Bonny Scotland.

Three days later he arrived home and it wasn't long before he came down to the farm to see me and ask me what I thought of his purchases.

I had to tell him: 'Do you want me to be honest and tell you the truth? They are worst three rams you have bought since I came here. When you told me you were going to Scotland I told you about the only ram I wanted, and I gave you the lot number and said that if you couldn't get that one then don't bother with anything else. It would not be a wasted journey as you were going up to Gleneagles anyway.' He wasn't expecting that sort of reply from me.

'Well, what's wrong with them?'

'Well, it's like this,' I told him. 'You and I have had the last ten years fully co-operating with everything that we have bought and sold, with results that any sheep breeder can be proud of. Three Royal Show champions, plus supreme and reserve champions at every show we have entered, plus the

Barrons Illustrious stud ram, bought for 1500 guineas

champion ram lamb at the Suffolk Sheep Society show and sale – that's a record that stands out and would be the envy of many breeders who have been trying to do as well for years. If I was to use rams like that it could set us back years. So if you'd like to come down to the shed in the morning I'll get our stock rams in and you will see what they are like in comparison. And my final word on the matter is that those crafty sods from across the border knew you were on your own and they took advantage of you. You should also remember that as President of the Suffolk Sheep Society, and with buyers coming from Europe, India, Africa and Norway, you have standards to maintain.' And that was my final word.

The next morning RLB came down to the yard. As I had said, I'd got our own stud rams in and penned them side by side. He looked at them and admitted that he was wrong and that what I had said was right. Fortunately no harm had been done; the rams I had were working well and I told him I should be able to get most of his money back next year by selling them as shearlings to commercial breeders. I don't think

Lionel thought much of me telling him the truth. I didn't see him again for some time after that, then I received a message that he wanted to see me in his office. I thought perhaps I had said too much and I was going to be given my cards, but anyhow, I was wrong. He called me in and was very pleasant, then he asked me to sit down. From what he told me, his gamekeeper has suffered a stroke while playing bowls. He had two very important shooting days coming up in November and he knew I enjoyed a bit of shooting as I always went out with the beaters when shoots were held on the farm. He allowed me to keep a gun in the Land Rover as there was a housing estate bordering on to the farm and so he provided me with a gun to keep stray dogs away. The keeper wouldn't shoot a stray cat, let alone a dog that was worrying sheep. My own policy regarding that sort of thing was to shoot first and ask questions afterwards. It paid off in the end after I had disposed of one or two illegal visitors.

To return to RLB, he wanted to ask me if I would be available to drive him to the shoot and act as his loader. The first shoot was with the Duke of Grafton, and the other was with a gentleman friend of his in Essex. I agreed on condition that I drove him there and back. They say that variety is the spice of life, and I was quite looking forward to acting as gamekeeper. It gave me something to pass the time during the latter half of the year while waiting for the first lambs to arrive in January 1977.

1977 was to be a year I shall not forget for a long time. On 9th February I was having a nap after lunch as I had been up most of the night with some late-lambing ewes, when a knock on the back door woke me up. It was the wife of the young man next door; she told me she thought there was a fire in the lamb yard. Not stopping even to put my Wellingtons on, I ran as fast as I could, to discover she was right. Patricia was following and I yelled to her to ring the fire brigade. I could see this was very serious. I pulled open the hurdles to let the sheep out, and then the ewes that were still in the pens were released. The ewes were soon out and the lambs followed them. I thought to myself thank goodness, at least we have saved the flock – but I had spoken too soon.

The sheep had to cross over the road that went through the farm and just as I thought they were all safe a car came down the road sight-seeing. This car frightened the lambs and some of them turned round and ran back into the burning yard. I shouted to the men to drive the rest of the flock onto the meadow while I dashed back to see if I could get the lambs out, but it was too late. The barn was the only place they knew. They had been born there and had never been anywhere else.

Under normal circumstances they would have been in a straw yard down the other side of the farm, but we had had a sharp winter and the pigeons and rabbits had eaten the kale and swedes that should have been their feed, so I had kept the ewes and lambs inside and hand fed them. In the meantime the fire brigade had arrived but there was little they could do as the barn was stacked full of hay and straw, and a combine was in there too. The combine's diesel tank had exploded which had made things much worse. I didn't know until the next day what losses we had suffered. In all we had lost 60 lambs. I was shattered.

To me, this was worse than foot and mouth, and I still think about it to this day. I am sure that the most likely cause of the fire was the infra-red heat lamp which hung over the pen where the cade lambs were ('cade' lambs being orphaned by the death of their mother or by being removed from a mother already burdened with two lambs). The ewes had rubbed against the hurdles of their pen and the lamp had slowly lowered nearer and nearer to the straw. When the hurdle fell, the lamp went down too and it didn't take many minutes before the fire got going. The loss of the lambs meant that there would not be much showing, if any, and it would cut down on the number of rams I would have available for sale. So we had to look ahead and make the best of a bad job. We still had the ewe flock and we hoped that 1979 would heal the wounds that the fire had caused.

RLB had been hoping that his son was going to take over the farm. During the months that followed, his son decided he didn't want anything to do with the farm. This upset RLB and as he was nearer to 80 than 70 he told me that if he could find someone who would buy the flock lock, stock and hurdles, he might be tempted to sell. Straightaway a farmer came to mind, who used to buy rams from this flock when I was at Lackford. His name was Robert Long. In a conversation I had had with him at the Suffolk Show, he said that if ever Mr Broad decided to sell the flock then he might be interested.

I think the fire was the last straw and finally made his mind up. I contacted Mr Long and he asked me to go and see him.

Feeding time for the orphans

9

Fordham

What was to be my last shearing season at Badlingham was to bring me into contact with John Taylor of Trinity Farm, Fordham, the next village about three miles down the road. I was asked if I could shear a few sheep for him. Little did I know at the time that I was about to meet a man who was to become a true friend and fellow showman for the next 20 years. Another good omen was when John's father came out to the shed with a bottle of whisky. I told him I'd better leave that until I'd finished the job otherwise I would be seeing double, but that bottle of whisky was not to be the last one we shared by a long way.

Eventually Pat and I decided to go and see Mr Long and have a look around Hall Farm. I contacted Robert Long to let him know we were coming to look at the house and discuss the terms of employment. This was settled without much bargaining, then he took us round to see the house – it was not a pretty sight. The builders were ripping the interior out and reconstructing it. Robert could see we were not happy with what was going on but he assured us that it would all be ready to move into in a couple of months. Now all he had to do was have a deal with Mr Broad. He also said he wouldn't buy the flock unless I came with it as part of the deal. So far, so good. The only thing that Mr Broad asked was that the Badlingham prefix of the flock remained the same. There was no trouble with this as the Suffolk Sheep Society regulations state that

Ken and his employer Robert Long
enjoy their success with a shearling ram,
Norfolk Show Champion 1988

if a flock is sold in its entirety then its prefix may only be changed once. So with everything sorted it was agreed that the changeover would take place in October 1979.

The move to Hall Farm took place without incident. The only thing that didn't go quite right was when we moved the sheep; the men who worked on the farm had set a fold with electric fencing which the ewes had not been used to. So what happened? The sheep walked straight through it, but luckily no harm was done, just a bit of strong language from the chaps who had set up the fence. After a bit of patience and a strong battery they soon got used to it, though one or two had stuck their noses on it. I think my poor old dog Moses came off the worst; it's only natural when a dog sees something different he'll cock his leg up on it, and that's just what he did. To say he got a bit of a shock is putting it mildly – he gave an awful yelp and he was home a lot quicker than he'd ever been before. I thought to myself, I must remember not to do that when I'm in need of a pee.

The move to Hall Farm was not too disruptive for the children. Charles was moving away from home to carry on with his career as a baker, and by this time Wendy was married and living in Chevington, a small village about six miles away. As for Simon, nothing ever bothered him and he was near the age of leaving school. He got sent home once for turning up at school with his hair dyed green; this was when punk bands were top entertainment. One weekend he brought a few of his friends home to the farm and asked if they could practise their music, if you could call it music. I told him that the only place he could go was into the garage, which was empty at the time, and to make sure that the door was shut. You never heard such a racket, and to make things worse, when I came down in the morning they were all lying asleep on the living room floor. To be fair to them, they never made a mess or left the place untidy though. Patricia, being the sort of mother she was, always made sure they had a good breakfast before they left.

Our youngest son, Duncan, was the quiet one. He still had a couple more years to do at school and he had not yet made up his mind what he wanted to do when he left. Unlike his brother, he preferred the quieter life, no punk bands, and he was not very sport-minded either, whereas Simon, as well as being involved in the noise in the garage, as I used to call it, was also very keen on sport. That was about the only thing Simon liked at school. On leaving school he remained a keen rugby player and joined the Bury St Edmunds Rugby Club.

I shall always remember my first Christmas at Hall Farm. It was the tradition for Mr and Mrs Long to invite all the men and their wives who lived on the farm to come round to the house for a seasonal drink, which was a very nice gesture. But when you walk into a room full of people, and the people are mostly those you work with and the drinks are free, it isn't very long before you forget how much you've had, especially when someone is walking round and topping up your glass when you're not looking. I was feeling perfectly all right in the warm room, but then came time to go home. As soon as I stepped outside, the cold air hit me and my legs buckled. According to Patricia, who wasn't very pleased with my behaviour, I had to be assisted home by my neighbours who laid me on the settee. I didn't remember anything else until that evening. Not only had I missed my Christmas dinner, but Patricia, as well as getting dinner ready for the rest of the family, had been in and out of the lamb yard penning up newborn lambs. So you can guess that when I eventually surfaced from my alcoholic sleep I was not very popular and was committed to the doghouse. It was a good job the lamb yard was all under cover and only 25 yards from our back door.

As well as the Suffolk flock, there was a large flock of commercial ewes on the farm. The shepherd was Connie Wisby; he was mostly addressed as Connie or Wis. This was an arable flock and lambed down in March indoors, before going out on to the two-year leys.

The next thing Robert Long and I had to sort out were the shows and the sales. We decided that the best thing to do was to show in those parts of the country where we sold the rams, and with the exception of exports, that was mainly East Anglia and Kent. The show season started in May with the South Suffolk, followed by the Hadleigh Show, then the Suffolk County Show and the South of England Show in June. The Royal Norfolk Show, the Kent Show and the East of England Show took place in July;

these were then followed by the Eastern Area Breed Sale on the Ipswich Showground. Then if you were lucky you might get a week or two to catch up with odd jobs at home.

With a flock of 150 breeding ewes with an average crop of lambs, I usually finished up with 80 to 100 rams to see each year. If you had a good sale year about 30% of these would be sold on the farm, most to regular customers. The rest of them went to what I call the bread and butter sales in the area, covered by the summer shows that we entered, starting with the sale at Bury St Edmunds in Suffolk at the end of August, then Findon in West Sussex and Ashford in Kent in September. My last trip always used to be to Leicester in October. It was like returning to my maternal home. I still had two brothers living there so I was assured of bed and breakfast. Believe it or not, on one trip up there I met a Mr Bert Higgs, the son of the owner of the farm on which I had seen my first Suffolk sheep way back in the 1920s.

The final event of the year was the Smithfield Fat Stock Show, held in

The author with a South Suffolk Champion Ram, 1992

Discussing the merits over a row of pens of stud rams

Earl's Court. I first started showing there in the late 1960s and in those days there were classes for pedigree breeds, so weights didn't make much difference. The championship nearly always went to either the Suffolk or the Scotch Blackface, and it was always quite an enjoyable week. Then they decided to alter the classes; all the classes were for any breed or crossbreed with the top weight being a maximum of 80lbs, and classes for lower weights; there were also new regulations that met you at the door. Vets were there to check the lambs for any illness, such as foot rot and orf (sore mouth), and if you had any wether lambs in your consignment they were inspected to make sure they had no testicles. Any of these faults and it was back into the lorry and you were sent home.

That was not the end of your worries; when you arrived at your pens the sheep stewards were there to weigh you in. If your weights were right you had nothing else to worry about, but if you were a little over or under you were given the option of having them weighed again in the morning. This meant that several pens of the heaviest lambs spent several hours being walked round and round the ring in the hope that they would shed a few pounds by the morning weigh-in. The funniest thing I saw one year was as I was walking round the pens looking at the opposition, I saw an old boy sitting in a pen and it looked as if he was drenching a lamb. I stood and watched from a distance and I could see that he was giving his three lambs bottles of water. Out of curiosity more than anything else I went up and asked him if anything was wrong. His reply was no, but his lambs were a bit short of the weight he needed so he thought a few pints of water each would do the trick. I guess he didn't think that the water would all be gone straight through them by the morning. You do meet some funny folk!

I decided to give up on Smithfield after that. You really needed a second, later, lambing if you wanted to show Suffolk lambs as they could reach the required weight in 12 to 14 weeks, and I could well do without lambing sheep down in July and August.

It was during the next couple of show seasons that John Taylor became a friend of mine for life. He used to come to the shows in an old truck with a few sheep and a settee and chairs in the back. Once the sheep had been unloaded the truck was cleaned out and converted into his bedroom, kitchen and bar. It was an unwritten law that no alcohol was consumed on the first night at the show (well, not much, anyway), as we had to be fit for the judging the next morning. But the next night would be a different story altogether: the whisky flowed fast and free well into the night. There was many a hangover the next morning.

As the years progressed, John's wagon became the focal point for the general get-together for the sheep lines. He converted an old oil drum into a barbeque and what went on that barbeque was nobody's business. After a few bottles of Scotch had disappeared I don't think our guests would have cared less as long as it looked good and tasted better. John eventually thought a bigger truck was needed as he was showing more sheep and the old truck was getting a bit crowded in the evenings. When he came to the show we could see the new truck was a bit different from the old one – it had a goods lift at the back. 'What's the idea of that lift, John?' I asked him.

'Well,' he replied, 'as you and Peter (Peter Roberts was a farming friend who showed Shropshire sheep and had joined our clan, going to the same shows as we did) are getting a bit long in the tooth, you might find it useful.'

John was a real friend. Peter or I often fell arse over head down the tailboard, especially as it was always dark when we left for our own sleeping quarters, which were lorries or trailers, so John thought it would be a good idea to have that goods lift attached before that happened.

The Suffolk Show was well known for its royal visitors so it was great to win the Suffolk Sheep Supreme Championship as you had to parade your winning sheep in the Grand Ring, where the trophies were given out by the royal visitors. I have seen many members of the royal family in the forty years that I have shown at the Suffolk Show: these have included HRH The Duchess of Kent twice, in 1968 and 1993; HRH Princess Alexandra twice, in 1981 and 1994; HRH The Princess of Wales in 1986; HRH Princess Margaret in 1995 and HRH The Princess Royal in 2004.

1987 was a year I was glad to see the back of. In February I had gone into hospital to have a hip replacement operation. I was only in hospital for five days and they did a marvellous job, but I was lucky I didn't mess it all up. After I had been home for a couple of days I decided to venture round to the lamb yard on my two sticks. There were still a few ewes that had still not lambed. As I walked into the yard an old ewe lay right in front of me; I had expected her to get up but she didn't move and I fell on top of her. Luckily for me I fell straight forward and no harm was done, but it put the wind up me. Then to make things even worse our eldest son Charles was taken ill and diagnosed with bowel cancer. He was working in London at the time and was admitted to hospital in Edgware. Fortunately they caught it in time and after a spell of convalescence he was back at work.

They say things happen in threes. Well, the third thing that happened was that in September our daughter and her husband informed us that they were thinking of emigrating to Australia. This was not the sort of news that Pat and I wanted to hear, but we have never told our children what they should do, nor have we ever stood in their way. So

RIGHT:
*Championship
Suffolk ram meets
Princess Alexandra,
1981*

BELOW:
*Princess Diana
meets Robert Long,
the author and
Mr Stennett at
the Championship
Suffolk Show in
1990*

on 24th October, on my birthday of all days, away they went.

Early in 1989 I opened the *Bury Free Press* one morning and what should I see but a photograph of Robert Long's son, Andrew, with a couple of cross-bred lambs in his arms. He had been telling the reporter about the sleepless nights he had been having (that was a laugh!). Anyhow, Robert got a phone call the next morning from a lady called Anna van Woerden, a retired midwife, offering to help. She was a Dutch spinster, tough as old boots, and a very hard worker. I think she did about two to three lambing seasons with the commercial flock before it was decided by Robert that she should help with the pedigree ewes. This was an advantage to me, as during that time Patricia had got to know her and she used to come and watch what I was up to in the sheep shed where I did my trimming and getting the sheep ready for the shows. This was a full-time job from May through to August, so when she offered to help I told her she could start as soon as she liked. She was very quick to grasp the routine of getting the sheep to lead and washing them and, depending on the weather, getting them dry. Then the hard work started, carding the wool and removing all the knots and curls ready for me to trim and get my hand shears to work, shaping up the sheep to make it look even better than it really was.

Anne became a dab hand at this but I would not let her have a go with the shears. It takes time and a lot of experience, and even with all the years that I have spent trimming my advice to newcomers is that you are never too old to learn a little bit more. I'll tell you something else too – the keen eyes of the older shepherds can tell by looking at a sheep who has trimmed it.

Having an extra pair of hands made a big difference as it gave me a bit more time to do other things. By now I had been put on the list of judges and Patricia had become a very keen member of her local Women's Institute and was eventually made the president. She was also a member of the West Suffolk Home Economics group and went on to win a bursary to go to Denham College in Oxfordshire. She got the bug for patchwork and quilting. After her second trip to Denham College she decided to resign as president of her local WI and concentrate on her patchwork. Sadly the local branch folded, but there was no stopping her now. She did a course at Otley College, in Suffolk. It took her two years to get her City and Guilds qualifications and in 1991 she started up a group in Fornham St Martin Village Hall, near Bury St Edmunds in Suffolk. This group is still going today, as strong as ever, making quilts and holding coffee mornings, raising money for various charities as well as teaching and helping people to quilt and sew.

My last trip down to the Findon Sheep Sale was to be the final one held there, as the sale was to be moved to the South of England Showground. It also coincided with Pat's birthday. On hearing this, Robert generously said I could take Pat down with me and spend the weekend down there, and he would pay our expenses. I didn't want asking twice. It was not very far from Brighton, so on arrival we penned the sheep then went off to look for a place to stay. We spotted a bed and breakfast sign and went to ask if they had any vacancies. It was a very posh place, and they told me they had a free room but only for the one night, and would we like tea on the lawn. I was lapping this up. I thought to myself, I don't have to pay for this so make the most of it, but it evened itself out in the end. At the sale the next day we met the wife of the gentleman who had been head Sheep Steward at the South of England Show for as long as I had been showing there. In the course of the conversation she mentioned that they had a cottage on their farm and we could stay the night there free of charge, so the weekend was going quite well. A look around Brighton, an evening meal in Shoreham, and back to a comfy cottage with all facilities for the night, then home the next day.

But that was the end of travelling to shows and sales. Robert had bought a new Range Rover and no one else was allowed to drive that. I was then going to get a van to take the sheep out in. It turned out to be a Ford van and the body was the trailer I had been using, welded onto the chassis of the Ford van. I was not a very happy shepherd, but worse was to come. It didn't mind short journeys, but when it came to a long haul it turned out to be a nightmare. After getting down to the South of England Show at Ardingly in Sussex safe and sound, the return journey was a different story. Saturday evening on the M25 is not the best time and

Trimming demonstration: Suffolk Show, 1986 the Author and Jimmy Cresswell

place to break down; just before the junction to turn off to Chelmsford the engine started to splutter. Luckily, I was near a lay-by and I managed to coax the van into it before it stopped completely. The lay-by just happened to have a phone box with a direct line to a garage just off the motorway. I told them I had a load of sheep in the vehicle, which I think convinced them that it was pretty urgent, as it wasn't very long before they had a mechanic on the scene. He had a good look around and said it looked like a fuel problem, but he couldn't do anything about it without taking it to the garage. Well, you couldn't do that without unloading the sheep, so the only way we could get home was to put the van with its load of sheep on the low-loader, and that's exactly how we eventually got home. Having a good mechanic on the farm, I was sure the van would soon be back on the road.

The next big event on the farm was the visit of 58 overseas farmers, from Australia, Belgium, France, Holland, Italy, Japan, New Zealand, Portugal, South Africa and the United States of America. Hall Farm was their last visit before they returned home, after a tour of British sheep farms organised by the Suffolk Sheep Society in its centenary year.

It was now decided by Robert Long and myself that the time was getting near for us to start to wind down as we were both getting on a bit. So we decided to have one more complete year at showing then have a reduction sale in 1993. I was to pick out 25 ewes to keep until I felt it was time to retire finally.

I was getting occasional judging invitations at the one-day local shows and Patricia was giving patchwork demonstrations at Ladies' Clubs. At one of her demonstrations she was asked if she knew anyone who could give a talk, and she told them it might well be worth asking me. I never

The Author checking that the right animals have been picked for the next show

gave it much thought as I had never given a talk to anyone, but it was not many days later that I received a letter from the secretary of a retired business men's club, the Probus Club, asking me if I would give a talk to its members. I agreed to their request and went along one afternoon, not knowing what I was going to talk about – no notes, just straight off the cuff. I thought to myself, I'd only done two things in my life, working with livestock and my war service, so I decided to give them a bit of both. And then I thought to myself, if I was a sportsman or some high-falutin personality, then I'd be getting paid for doing this sort of thing, so why not me? But I held my tongue on that subject and spoke to them for about an hour and a half. It was well received by all and they really enjoyed it once I'd got over a nervous start. Then the secretary came up and asked me what my fee was, which caught me off guard for a few seconds, but I quoted him a sum of money which he agreed to without question.

This started the ball rolling and word got round. I was getting requests from all over West Suffolk, including Bury St Edmunds, Mildenhall, Newmarket and Thurston. As most of the meetings took place in the evenings it suited me well as it didn't interfere with my work during the day.

But back to my last full showing year, 1993. Things were going well. 1992 had been a good year and if 1993 was going to be as good I couldn't want a better finish on my retirement. Nor would it do the reduction sale any harm later in the year. As the sale catalogue said:

The sale arises due to Ken Riggall's decision to 'wind down' his activities and reduce his workload, although he hopes to remain active in the sheep world for many years to come. He will, of course, be in attendance at the viewing and the sale and will be happy to provide prospective purchasers with as much background information as they might need.

The Badlingham Flock
To most people involved with sheep, the Badlingham Flock requires no introduction – not only is it one of the oldest Suffolk flocks in the country but has also scooped up regional and national awards for many years.
Ken Riggall the shepherd has become a familiar face on the show and sale circuit and under his care and experience the quality and achievement of the flock have set the highest possible standards.
The flock, originally known as the Yeldham Flock, was established in 1906 by Goodchild and remained in this ownership until 1953 when it was sold to D. P. Gough of Lackford. After twelve years the flock was sold to R. L. (Lionel) Broad at Badlingham, near Newmarket

– hence its present title. After this Ken Riggall was to start achieving some of his greatest triumphs with the flock and went with the sheep to Robert Long in 1979 at Fornham St Martin and during his time at Hall Farm the flock has become one of the best known in the country with breeding replacements going throughout Britain and abroad.

Recent successes include :-

1993
South Suffolk Show – Inter-breed Champion, Champion Suffolk, 4 firsts

Hadleigh Show – Champion Suffolk, Reserve Suffolk

Suffolk Show – Supreme Champion, Reserve Supreme Champion, Male Champion, Female Champion, Inter-breed Champion, 3 firsts, 2 seconds
South of England Show – Inter-breed champion, Breed Champion, 2 firsts, 1 second

Royal Norfolk Show – Male reserve Champion, Female Reserve Champion, 2 firsts

Kent Show – Inter-breed Champion, Breed Champion, 4 firsts, 1 second

East of England Show – Reserve Breed Champion, 2 firsts, 1 second

1992
South of England Show – Breed Champion

Suffolk Show – Reserve Champion, 2 firsts, 2 seconds

Royal Norfolk Show – 2 Reserve Champions, 1 Champion, 5 firsts, 4 seconds

Kent Show – Inter-breed Champion, breed champion, 5 firsts, 2 seconds

East of England Show – 2 firsts

Eastern Area Flock Competition – Winners 1989, 1991, 1992

The reduction sale was set to take place on 14th October at Hall Farm. I drew out the 25 ewes I was to keep to give me something to do for another year or two. The sale went very well, with buyers from the Midlands and the South of England. Ewes made a good general trade with a top price of £450, and ewe lambs topping £200. I was well pleased, knowing that I had creamed off 25 of the best ewes, with a buyer waiting in the wings for them as soon as I said I was finally ready to say I'd had enough.

LEFT:
Interview for Radio Suffolk

BELOW:
John Taylor, Patricia and Ken Riggall at Ken's retirement in 1988

10

Culmination of a career

The word soon got round that I had a bit of time on my hands, with judging invitations coming in thick and fast and people wanting advice. The first major show I was asked to judge at was the Lincolnshire County Show, where I was asked to judge the inter-breed championship and the best sheep in the show. Patricia came with me to these events as she was a very good navigator. After spending the night in a hotel in Lincoln we set off for the showground, which I knew quite well as I had shown there for several years during the 1970s. But this time it was a bit different in that it was my own name in the show catalogue and not the name of the person I was working for. Of course, Lincolnshire was the home of my forefathers; it was just about the only place you would see the name of Riggall. On reporting to the stewards' office I was soon being asked if I was related to the Riggalls of Tathwell, a small village just outside Louth. I told them that my grandfather farmed there and that my father was born there. I was then directed to the sheep ring by the head sheep steward, whom I knew quite well, having shown sheep there in the 1970s for R. L. Broad. One or two of the breeders recognised me and sure enough, they made a prediction that the Suffolks were going to win. But after nearly 50 years of facing judges all over the country and experiencing some of them who judged the shepherds before the sheep, as they knew who worked for whom, I was there to judge the interbreed championship for the best sheep in the show. It's a bit different today as in some cases it's down to who has the biggest cheque book. I have to admit that had there been a Suffolk there good enough I should have been only too pleased to have given it the championship, but, alas, it was not to be. I gave the top prize to a Bleu de Maine.

Whatever you do, you can't please everyone, but you should never criticise the judge (at least, not so as he can hear you), as you never know when you will have to face him again. After all, whoever it may be, he's only there to please himself on the day and no one else in particular.

1994 was a quiet year. With only a small flock of 25 pedigree Suffolks to look after I had time on my hands, but not for long. I was now only showing at the Suffolk and Norfolk County Shows. Requests for advice and visits to small flocks started to come in. I was asked to judge at two more shows in Lincolnshire: Deeping in June and Heckington in July. Patricia and I will always remember the Heckington show because of the entertainment at our overnight stay. We had decided to stay the night before the show at the local inn. It seemed a nice place, the food was good and the company quite amicable, and so we booked a room for the night. As the evening wore on, all of a sudden the place began to fill up. It was then that we discovered that a wedding party was booked into the lounge and a DJ was there. To make it even more unpleasant, it was right underneath the bedroom we had booked. It seemed at the time that the racket went on for most of the night.

1995 was to be my 38th Suffolk Show. Not until the morning of the show was I told that I was to be presented with a framed certificate by HRH Princess Margaret to mark 38 years of sheep husbandry. To top that, when I got home from the Suffolk Show there was a letter waiting for me from the secretary of the northern branch of the Suffolk Sheep Society, asking me if I would judge the flock competition for the northern area later in the year. I didn't take long in answering in the affirmative. In the meantime I was getting several enquiries for advice and call-outs to put people on the right track who were starting small flocks, plus teaching a couple of ladies the art of trimming.

The first call I had was from a Mr Chalk, who by profession was a gynaecologist of the top bracket with a business in Harley Street. He had bought a house at Whepstead, near Bury St Edmunds, with several acres of grass and he wanted to know roughly how many ewes it would keep, and could I get him a ram. When I started to reel off what else was involved, like drenching for worms, injecting against pulpy kidney, shearing, dipping and foot trimming, I think he began to wonder what he had taken on. The only thing he said he wouldn't have any problem with would be the lambing, as he dealt with that sort of thing every day. He said he didn't mind going ahead with the project as long as I was able to be on call.

The next call I had was from a farmer out at Pakenham, Mr R. Whitwell. He told me he had just got rid of his herd of milking cows and had bought some sheep to keep the grass down. He wanted someone to shear them and he needed a ram. I obliged him on both accounts. He told me he had no shepherd and asked whether he could call on me for help if he needed it, which was no problem to me as he was only a couple of miles away. As time went by, I found out that Mr Whitwell was a countryman of the old school and liked the old fashioned way of life. There was nothing he liked better than to walk among his livestock with a pocketful of sheep nuts. The old ram was always first in line to have his head scratched, which eventually became his downfall. He started to draw back when Mr Whitwell went to feed him; playfully at first, then one day as Roy Whitwell turned to leave, the ram hit him from behind, full force, which put him in hospital. The next thing I heard of the ram was when I got a phone all from one of Mr Whitwell's farming friends in Walsham-le-Willows. He was asking whether I knew anything about a Suffolk ram that I had sold to Roy Whitwell. My reply was that if it was the ram I thought it was, then he should get it to market as soon as he could before it did him any injury. I explained what had happened to Roy. With the lady in question being of small frame I'm sure that ram would have done her a lot more damage if he had caught her unawares. I think Roy was keen to be rid of the ram and had not forewarned the lady.

I think the next call-out was the worst I had seen in all my shepherding life. Robert Long's son came to see me as I was eating my evening meal and asked me if I would go and look at some sheep that one of his friends kept out near Ixworth. It appeared the sheep had got fly trouble.

I said, 'By the sound of what you're telling me, I'd better go as soon as possible.' Getting my medication and shears, I got the farm van out.

On arrival at the farm I had never seen sheep and lambs in such a sorry state. They were literally being eaten alive by maggots. I did not know where to start. First of all I asked the farmer whether he had any fly dip or spray. He replied that he hadn't. By this time his wife had arrived on the scene and her told her to go into Central Wool Growers in Bury St Edmunds and get some as quickly as possible. While she had gone I thought that the best thing I could do was to give them an injection. The ewes were in a terrible state, with huge patches of raw flesh on four of them. Their lambs, which were only a few weeks old, were covered in maggots where they had rubbed up against their mothers when trying to suckle. Next I had to get my hand shears out and clip off as much wool as possible where the maggots had gone in. By this time the lady of the house had arrived back and had managed to get the right dip. As there was no dipping bath we had to mix it up in pails and rub it into the fleece by hand. I told the gentleman in question before I left that what we had done was only temporary and he should get them dipped properly as soon as possible. I never heard another thing from the farm, but I should be very much surprised if they all survived.

My final show season was approaching and as I only had a small number of ewes left I would only be doing the county show and a couple of local one-day shows. That was my plan, but it didn't quite work out that way. I had kept one stud ram back to cover the ewes that I had retained, but unfortunately a week before I had wanted to put him in with the flock he had got on his back in the night and I found him the next morning with his legs in the air and as stiff as a board – in other words, he was dead. So I did a bit of phoning round and Mr Ian Bradshaw came to my rescue. I had done some trimming for him in the past so he said I could borrow one of his rams and he would bring it to the farm. When he arrived with it I was not very happy, but I had no option but to say how pleased I was that he could help me. Without more ado I turned him in with the ewes and hoped for the best. In any case, I would have to wait five months to find that out.

The next trip out was judging the Suffolk flocks in the northern area, taking Patricia with me as the navigator. Conny Wisby was to look after the sheep, and our eldest son Charles was to look after the house and the dogs, cats and chickens. This was going to be something quite different, not a bit like being at a county show. Straight up the A1 to Doncaster for our first flock, at the home of the Euro MP. He was a nice chap but for some reason his sheep were all over the place; but I was not there to criticise. After a good look round he asked us in for lunch and then gave me directions for the next visit which was to Low Santon Farm, Appleby, near Scunthorpe, in Lincolnshire. On arrival we were invited to spend the night at Mr Sandy Fraser's home, which was much appreciated as it had been a long day.

Next morning, after a first class breakfast and a final look at the Santon flock, we headed towards Grimsby. We were met by the next flock owner, who showed us his flock then directed us to another flock in the same area. After that it was Hexham and Heddon-on-the-wall for more visits.

Then we headed along Hadrian's Wall towards Carlisle. On arrival at the farm we were greeted by several dogs and the owner of the sheep, and if I may say so a bit too cocky he was for my way of thinking. We had hardly got into the field when in the course of the conversation he made the remark that he usually wins the flock competition. Well, from what I had seen so far he wasn't likely to do so this time. He offered to put us up for the night. I apologised, saying that I had to get to the next flock while it was still light and that was at Driffield, just north of York, at a place with the unusual name of Uncleby Wold, Kirby Underdale. The two flocks were not too far apart.

The flock at Driffield belonged to a Mr Twiddle, who at that time was the largest turkey producer in the country. You couldn't miss his place. As you got near, a huge model of a white turkey greeted you at the gate.

You don't expect a wealthy business man to be at home on such a minor occasion, but I knew his shepherd and it seemed he was in the same position as I was. His flock had been reduced prior to being sold on the shepherd's retirement. We had a good chin-wag and a cup of tea and after looking at his sheep I could see that he had selected a few of his best ewes to give him something to do until he really felt like retiring. Then it was on to my last visit, to Uncleby Wold, to spend the night at John Midgely's. I knew John's father from way back in the 1960s. Tom Midgely was one of the old school and like me he was a great believer in the old-fashioned Suffolks. He always said that true Suffolks were bred in their home county and I still believe that it is the same today. After many successful years at the major shows and sales, Tom had lost his eldest son Dennis quite suddenly. This was a big blow to Tom as Dennis had been his right hand man and was good at his job. It then fell to his younger son John to fill the gap, which over a period of years he has done very well; he now owns his own flock, and is ably assisted by his wife Liz. After looking at his sheep we sat down to a good Yorkshire meal and a good night's sleep, before setting off the next morning for the journey home.

It had been a good week, except for the fog every morning. Not only had it made it difficult to find places, it also meant we didn't get the chance to see the countryside, and it was always mid-morning before it had cleared. The morning we went over the Humber Bridge, we couldn't see either side which was most disappointing as we had been looking forward to the views. Just to make things worse, as we got onto the M1 it came down again, so we decided to pull into a motel and make a fresh start in the morning.

On arriving home it was nice to find everything as it should be. Connie had kept the sheep all the right way up and Charles had kept things in order in the house and garden. My plans to retire seem to have come unstuck as the more I talked about it, the more my friends urged me to keep on for a bit longer. As I mentioned before, a lot would depend on my next crop of lambs. When they arrived, I think I can honestly say that in my opinion they were a cracking bunch, which just goes to show that it's not always the best lookers that produce the goods – it's what they leave as offspring that's important.

Getting back to the flock judging competition in the Northern Area, after a session of adding up the points, I decided to award the top prize to the Santon flock owned by Sandy Fraser. It was a well matched flock of the type of sheep I like, and after travelling over 1,000 miles I had seen a lot of good Suffolks, but those were the ones that had caught my eye. A few weeks later Sandy put the flock on view to members and friends of the Suffolk Sheep Society, and my wife and I had to go back to Santon to present the prize. A good friend of mine, Jim Cresswell, who kept a small flock at Wattisfield near Diss in Norfolk, offered to drive us which suited me very well.

The quality of the lambs from the ram I had been loaned by Mr Bradshaw so impressed me that I decided to stay on for another year if I could use him again. He replied in the affirmative. I'm not saying that we were breeding champions like we had been over the past years, but I was enjoying the fellowship of my fellow showmen, especially John Taylor. In between times, two more judging appointments came along. I was asked to go and judge at the Southern Area Suffolk sheep club's Open Day. This was a bit different as I had to go at the end of April and judge the ewes while they still had their lambs on them. So, packing our overnight bags, Pat and I set off for Oxford and our first stop at the flock of Mr Jack Cook and his son John, based at Abbey Farm, Eynsham. We were to stay the night there. The best news we heard that day was that we were to be driven round the different flocks by Mr Filimore and another member of the club, Mr Brian Dyer, who kept a small flock in Bentworth Alton in Hampshire. Brian picked us up from our Oxford address after looking at Mr Cook's flock. We headed back to Hampshire, calling on two more flocks on our way back to Brian's house and refreshments. It was to be as far as we were going to go at this stage so it was a case of feet up and relax.

As I sat talking to Brian I became aware of the continuous chiming of clocks. On looking round I could see clocks all round the room. I never said anything to Brian but he could see that I was curious and he asked if they bothered me. Well, if they did I couldn't very well say so – everyone to their own. Anyway, he told me he had something that might interest me in the spare room. On opening the door I was confronted by several motorbikes of vintage varieties. That was a sight that will always remind me of my visit to his home, aptly named Crossways.

The next day he took me round to the remaining five flocks. These were small hobby flocks owned by people I had never heard of, travelling through West and East Sussex and finishing up near Guildford in Surrey.

Then it was back to Jack Cook's for the night before heading home the next morning. 1995 was to be my last season of showing, with the remainder of the flock being transferred to its new owner, Mr C. Kniestedt, from near Lewes in Sussex. It was a sad occasion for me to see them being loaded up, but time catches up with us all eventually. My time, I hoped, would be spent passing on my knowledge to up-and-coming younger people wishing to learn a few of the finer points in the art of showing sheep.

The 1998 Suffolk Show was to prove to be quite a send-off. During the judging, I was introduced to the Princess Royal. Then I was told that I was to be presented to the Duke of Edinburgh at the Royal Show and that the Suffolk Sheep Society was to make a presentation to me at the Royal Show on the same day. The president at that time was Mr Sandy Fraser, who presented me with a Border Fine Arts family group of Suffolk Sheep, which I shall always treasure.

As for the Suffolk Show, things were going on as normal. Then Patricia,

Ken and Patricia Riggall at Buckingham Palace with Ken's MBE

who would usually be going home around 4 or 5 o'clock, suggested that as this was to be our last show we should have a walk round, just for old times' sake. Little did I know that this was a put-up job, as she said she wanted to be back at the sheep lines by 6 p.m. It never dawned on me what was about to take place; on arrival back at the sheep I could not believe my eyes. John's barbeque was smoking away, and tables had been set up like a huge buffet. This had all been organised by the Suffolk Sheep Club in recognition of my retirement after 50 years showing Suffolk Sheep. The drinks table was very prominent, with several bottles of Famous Grouse, and to top this occasion I was presented with a cut glass whisky decanter with my name and career engraved into it. At this stage I was feeling a very happy and proud man, with my wife Patricia beside me as she had been for the past 50 years. I was delighted to have her there to share this occasion with me. I could not have wished for a better finish to my career. Not that I was going to hang my shears up quite yet. The difference was that I would be able to please myself where I go and what I do.

On 13th November 1998, I received the following letter from Number 10, Downing Street, London, SW1A 2AA:

From the Secretary for Appointments
In Confidence

Dear Sir,

The Prime Minister has asked me to inform you in strict confidence, that he has had it in mind, on the occasion of the forthcoming list of New Year's Honours, to submit your name to the Queen with a recommendation that Her Majesty may be graciously pleased to approve that you be appointed a Member of the Order of the British Empire.

Before doing so, the Prime Minister would be glad to be assured that this would be agreeable to you. I should be grateful if you would let me know by completing the enclosed form and sending it to me by return of post.

If you agree that your name should go forward and the Queen accepts the Prime Minister's recommendation, the announcement will be made in the New Year's Honours List. You will receive no further communication before the list is published.

I'm sure I didn't need to be asked a question like that twice. I could hardly get the necessary reply in the post quick enough. It was going to be a long six weeks before I heard anything else, but I knew it was no good thinking that far ahead. I had not heard of anyone else who has spent his working life looking after sheep getting an honour that I would be receiving. I just could not believe it would happen. To make matters worse, this was going to be the first Christmas in 50 years that I would not have any newborn lambs to celebrate the New Year. But it was all about to change.

New Year's Eve 1998 will be a date that I shall always remember. The phone never seemed to stop ringing. First I had a phone call to inform me that I had been awarded the MBE. The local paper, the *Bury Free Press*, phoned, wanting to interview me. As soon as I had put the phone down, the *East Anglian Daily Times* telephoned to ask the same questions. By now I was beginning to believe it myself. Then Anglia Television said they were coming to see me, and then the following day BBC East TV called to see me too. By now I was convinced that it was actually going to happen to me and it was simply a matter of waiting to find out when.

1999 was starting off like a dream, and to put the icing on the cake, I was then asked if I would judge the Suffolk Sheep classes at the Suffolk Show in 2000. What more could I ask for?

I soon found out that retirement for me was only a word, and one whose meaning I didn't know, as far as I was concerned. There were several small flocks within a reasonable distance from where I lived, and I was being called upon quite frequently. Could I come and have a look at a ewe that was in difficulty lambing; would I have time to shear a few sheep; would it be possible to show us how to prepare a sheep for showing. Now, I don't mind helping anyone who really needs help and who is keen to have a go, but there are still people about with an acre or two of grass who think all you have to do is to buy a few sheep, put them on a paddock, shut the gate and they'll look after themselves. I remember going to shear a few sheep for a man near Newmarket. He brought out a large Jacob ram, with horns about two feet long, and half a dozen ewes. He said they hadn't been shorn for 2 years because he couldn't find anyone to do them. I told him he was bloody lucky they hadn't been eaten alive with maggots. Jokingly, I told him I told him I would do them but I would have to charge him double. He must have thought I meant what I said, as he duly paid me double, not that I was complaining.

During the last three years of showing and judging at local shows I was asked if I would visit the flock of Val and Joe Walton at East Bergholt in Suffolk. As this was a new flock I decided to go and have a look, and I was quite surprised at what I saw. It was only a small flock but several of the older ewes had come from the Badlingham flock, having been purchased at the reduction sale. I could see that it had the makings of a good flock. Val, who looked after them, was pretty keen, and she asked if I could teach her to trim as she wanted to do a bit of showing. I arranged to pay her a couple of visits a year, by which time we would know if she could do the job or not. She took to it better than I expected which was a good thing as I was having trouble with my hip and so was not able to do any more for her. I had been told I need a hip replacement and couldn't cope with any more sheep work. I was already doing as much as I could.

I was already assisting another lady flock owner, Gail Sprake, with her flock of Southdowns. I had met her at Easton Farm Park where I was giving a demonstration of trimming, and she had asked me for my advice on preparing her sheep for shows. That was way back in the mid-1990s and I have been helping her ever since. With help from her husband Michael, and daughters Philippa and Ellie, the flock has gone from strength to strength, winning the National Breed Championship for Southdowns in 2004.

On 29th January 1999 the letter I had been waiting for arrived, telling me that an Investiture was to be held at Buckingham Palace and that my attendance was requested on 16th March 1999.

I was to arrive between the hours of 10.00 and 10.30 a.m. I was allowed to bring three guests: my wife Patricia and my two eldest sons, Charles and Simon. Duncan, our youngest son, was to drive us up to the palace, and he volunteered to stay with the car as the rules stated that if you parked in the palace car park then someone had to remain with the car.

This was a day I shall remember for the rest of my life. It was just like Christmas. The amount of cards and letters coming through the letterbox was fantastic. They came from as far away as USA, Canada and Australia, from family members and from people whose Suffolk sheep I had first started to work for in 1947. It truly was amazing. Auctioneers, farmers and people from all walks of life wrote to me. Tom, the husband of one of my daughter's friends, wrote a poem especially for me. I thought it was so good that I have to include it in my book.

THE SHEPHERD

In days gone by when sheep were sheep
And shepherds watched at night,
Before the days when men would sleep
And rise at first daylight,
There came a man from far away
To Suffolk's country life,
With dogs and cats, he came to stay,
With sheep, and Pat, his wife.

As time went on he made his name
At every county show.
As Kenneth Riggall rose to fame
The Badlingham flock would grow.
Behind the scenes the work was hard
With breeding, grooming, tending,
With long nights in the breeding yard
The jobs were never-ending.

His life, his work, and ways have let
His reputation grow.
With fewer sheep he now can get
To judge instead of show,
And now he's been invited to
Receive Royal acclaim.
An MBE now added to
The Riggall hall of fame.

CONGRATULATIONS KEN

Tom Morgan

On arrival at the palace, the ushers directed the guests to the ballroom and seated them in rows quite close to where the Queen would make the investiture. The people receiving their insignia were directed to the picture gallery and lined up according to what decoration they were going to get. Each recipient then files in to the ballroom in alphabetical order, bows to the Queen, shakes her hand and has a little chat. She then pins your decoration onto your coat, then you give her another bow, step back a few paces and walk out. I never thought the day would come when I would be doing that.

The remainder of 1999 seemed rather boring after that, but I had a busy year ahead in 2000. I had been asked to judge at several shows and I was really looking forward to the Suffolk Show in Ipswich. I was also judging at the Surrey County Show and at the Tendring Hundred Show near Colchester. This would bring back some memories as the Tendring Hundred Show was the first show at which I showed Suffolk sheep way back in 1948. Then it was on to the East of England Show at Peterborough.

2001 was a disastrous year for livestock in general. Foot and mouth disease was reported up in the North and, having been a victim of the disease myself in 1951, I knew just how they must be feeling: waking up in the morning and finding a lifetime's work and breeding skill gone or very soon would be. This outbreak seemed to be getting about for the same reasons as it did in 1951 – lack of knowledge in spotting it unless you have actually seen it. So of course you have to take blood tests, and by the time you get the results a lot more stock has been infected. But I think the main problem was that a lot of people who were sent out to check on stock had never seen foot and mouth, and in that part of the country sheep were thick on the ground. It was not spotted soon enough to prevent a major outbreak and thousands of healthy sheep in my opinion were condemned through sheer panic and bad organisation. In the latter part of the outbreak the ministry were paying a lot of people to have their sheep killed if they considered them to be a health risk, no matter where they lived. This was taken advantage of by some flock masters when they found out they would be paid a lot more than they would get if the animals were put on the market. I shall say no more regarding this subject, but if anyone was to write a book on the outbreak of 2001 I would say it ought to be entitled *Slaughter of the Innocents*.

It seems a strange coincidence that I should start my career as a shepherd with a pedigree flock over 50 years ago, and finally retire with the same problem affecting the country in 2001. Thank goodness I hadn't got a flock to lose this time.

My boss's son was now running the farm and policies were changing. Like so many young farmers he didn't want any livestock, but I wasn't too worried about that. I was living in a tied cottage, having a gentleman's agreement that I could remain there as long as I could climb the stairs. So you could say I was a mite surprised when a note was slipped through the letter box, giving me six months' notice and telling me that full rent and council tax were payable. On contacting the farm office, nobody had anything to say on the matter. So much for loyalty, a word you don't hear today.

After 20 years of success at shows and sales with the sheep, and building up the reputation of the Badlingham flock as a flock of high quality not only in the British Isles but also abroad, I should not have had to end this way. It's at times like this you find out who your true friends are, and over the years at the shows and sales my wife and I have made many friends.

Patricia has been my rock and I know I could not have had such a successful life without her. How she has always put up with everything – for that I shall be eternally grateful. I often sit and wonder why she put up with the terrible living conditions for the first ten years of our marriage. Still, I've always said it isn't only money that makes you rich. It is the love of a good woman and coming home at the end of a day to a happy family.